A CENTURY OF PROGRESS SERIES

OUR MINERAL CIVILIZATION

BY

THOMAS T. READ, E.M., Ph.D.

*Vinton Professor of Mining Engineering,
School of Mines, Columbia University,
New York*

Baltimore, 1932
THE WILLIAMS & WILKINS COMPANY
IN COOPERATION WITH
THE CENTURY OF PROGRESS EXPOSITION

COMPOSED AND PRINTED AT THE
WAVERLY PRESS, INC.
FOR
THE WILLIAMS & WILKINS COMPANY
BALTIMORE, MD., U. S. A.

To M. C. R.

CONTENTS

PREFACE

Among the many curious phenomena of human conduct and reasoning is the wide-spread agreement, in literature and oratory, that the present is a materialistic age, although a moment's intelligent consideration of the catalogue of any library at once reveals that the great bulk of literature deals with emotions and conduct rather than with material things. The problems of the moment, such as financial depression and prohibition are, for example, problems of human relations and conduct, rather than problems of the material substances gold and ethyl alcohol. Much modern thinking is poisoned with the ancient superstition that material things have inherent power to affect men, instead of recognizing that their effects upon men depend upon what use is made of them. A sane control of human conduct and relations must be based on a clear understanding of the true function of material things in human life.

Meticulous persons may question my use of the word mineral throughout the text, since geologists and mineralogists restrict its application to "a homogenous substance of definite composition found ready-made in nature and not directly a product of the life or decay of an organism." But as this is a popular discussion it seems not only permissible but even more suitable to use it in the popular sense, so familiar in the game of "Twenty Questions," of anything which is neither animal nor vegetable, thus including many things that are not found ready-made in nature, and avoiding the question of homogeneity and definite composition, which leads us into difficulties if we attempt to apply it strictly to metals as used in industry.

It goes without saying that I am indebted to the authors of almost all that I have read in this field, and under even more of obligation to many friends who have read some or all of the final text and commented upon it. Being friends, they will not insist on acknowledgement and readers, I assume, care little where an author got his ideas.

THOMAS T. READ.

New York, N. Y.
June 30, 1932.

CHAPTER I

A CENTURY OF PROGRESS IN MINERAL CIVILIZATION

ONE of the most striking characteristics of our twentieth century civilization is the large and growing use of minerals. The utilization of mineral substances to maintain and improve the conditions of living for humankind is so old a phenomenon that archeologists sometimes divide the periods of human development into ages of stone, bronze, and of iron. This division is misleading in two ways. It is difficult to make such a correlation between time and mineral substances as it implies, and it does not bring into the picture quantitative relationships that are of great importance. In referring to the present as an age of iron and steel one may be aware that the world production of pig iron amounts to about 100 pounds per capita yearly, without sensing the fact that nearly one-half the population of the globe live on the basis of about 10 pounds each yearly, while in the United States in 1929 the annual requirement of new iron and steel was about 1000 pounds each. This, again, is many times the an-

1

nual per capita requirements in the United States of a century earlier.

Seen in this way, the past century emerges as one in which there has been a tremendous increase in the quantity of mineral substances utilized by man. This has not resulted from a simple expansion of the old uses, but has in many cases come about from the discovery of new uses to which mineral substances can be put. The latter, in turn, has often sprung from a more precise knowledge of the nature and properties of mineral substances, permitting the devising of means whereby their properties can be modified and controlled.

Such a general statement must at once be qualified by pointing out while it is true of many mineral substances it is not true of others, and in its application is quite uneven. In the case of gold no important new uses have been found, and the world has always willingly received all the gold that it has been able to produce. Lead, on the other hand, is now largely used for purposes that were unknown a century ago, and the annual requirement has been correspondingly increased. Coal can serve only the purpose of furnishing heat and energy. Between 1870 and 1900 our consumption of coal doubled approximately every decade, while from 1920 to 1930 it did not increase at all, so that we now have the capacity to produce yearly twice as much coal as we are using. Petroleum at the beginning of the century was scarcely used at all, seventy-five years ago it came into wide use for illumination and lubrication, and fifty years later the development of the internal combustion engine created a new use that has already become the most important. In discussing the manner in which minerals have served to improve the conditions of existence for human beings it will be necessary to take them up separately, after the general point has been made that it has been through the use of minerals that man has most notably enlarged his capacities.

As an example of how these capacities have been enlarged, let us consider the motile function. Man's use of sailing vessels to move himself and his goods from one place to another was the only major improvement over his native capacity for motion that he made in thousands of years; for while beasts of burden and stage-coaches relieved man of effort they did not enable him to move much faster or progress much farther in a day than he could unaided. But the coal-iron combination known as the railroad, scarcely more than a century old, enables him to travel as far in an hour as he previously could in a day, while the petroleum-mineral aggregates known as automobiles and airplanes have multiplied the speed of a railroad from two to five times. Such a development as this has far-reaching and profound social results. Food supplies, for example, can be brought from great distances at a relatively small increase of cost, not only widening the market of a producing area, but also permitting a better balance and greater variety in the food supply of a community.

Another illustration of enlarged capacity can be seen in the function of communication. Sending messages through metal wires has greatly increased the range as well as the speed of transmission as compared with the age-old method of smoke signals, while the utilization of radio waves (themselves a development from the perception of physical properties and the application of mineral substances to their utilization) now permits simultaneous reception of a message at an almost infinite number of distant points, far beyond the previous range of audibility and visibility.

The making of records has always been largely based on the use of minerals, and the earliest ones that still remain are usually carved stone or burned clay. The invention of paper and ink changed this for a time but the printing press and the production of ink from natural gas has made it again dependent on the use of minerals. And minerals have made vision independent of time and place. No one could see the coronation of a medieval king except the persons then present; but the ceremonies attendant on the proclamation of George V as Emperor of India were not only seen through the whole world, by the aid of moving pictures, but can still be seen at any later time. Now the sounds as well as the sights can be preserved.

I might go on multiplying examples, but surely enough has been said to indicate that while minerals have always been important to man in enabling him to fulfil his desires, the past century is one that stands pre-eminent for the variety as well as the quantitative importance of these uses. There is not a single mineral substance of which the quantity used in the past century is less than the total of all the centuries that preceded. For many of them the principal uses are to supply needs that have arisen within the century, and these uses enable men to do many things that previously were quite beyond their power. So man by his mastery of minerals, has increased his own stature.

CHAPTER II

MODERN MAGIC

A<small>LADDIN</small>'s lamp is the age-old popular symbol of magic power. Conscious of a sense of inadequacy to the great universe about him man finds not only romance but a sense of comfort in dreaming of a magic force that might enable him to fulfill his every wish. So appealing to credulity is the belief in magic that many people seem unable to perceive the romance in the fact that we actually have available an equally remarkable source of power, not a lamp to rub but something to burn; something which enables us to fulfill our wishes in ways so instantaneous and so complete that, were it not that we understand how it operates, the result would be as astonishing and as romantic as the tale of the magic talisman. Entering your house at night you can flood it with soft light at the touch of a button. An action so familiar to you would have appeared just as remarkable to Aladdin as anything he could, according to the fairy tale, have done with his magic lamp. "Ah, yes," you say, "that is the almost magical force of electricity." "Not at all,"

I reply, "it is coal, because without coal there would have been no electricity; when you wished for light you did the equivalent of rubbing a lump of coal, and your room was lighted. There is as much romance in that as in any fairy tale if only you can see it."

How great this source of power is but few people seem to appreciate. It is easy to show by simple calculations that approximately half of all the work done in the world today is done in our United States, which contains only one-twentieth of the population of the world. How can so few people do so much work? They cannot, most of it is done for them by machines that multiply the capacities of men. Two pounds of coal, properly applied, will do the work of a man for a day. Almost two-thirds of the work done in the United States is done by coal and most of the other third is done by petroleum and natural gas. Every person in the United States has not simply a magic talisman but rather forty invisible genii, of one man-power each, to do his bidding. Is it any wonder, therefore, that the people of the United States have produced so much of the world's goods as to excite the wonder of the world?

The production of coal is the principal mining industry of the United States, which is the same as saying it is the principal mining industry of the world, since our country with its one-twentieth part of the world's population produces nearly half of all the world's coal, or somewhat under two million tons daily. The size of this industry is more easily visualized when I remind you that the coal dug underground, hoisted to the surface and distributed to the consumers in our country each year is greater in volume than the total amount of material that was dug out of the Panama Canal in all the years it was under construction. Simply to do the job of bringing this enormous amount of material to the surface employs (in good years) over 500,000 persons, while its surface transportation and distribution to consumers engages the activities of many more. Coal constitutes, in fact, nearly one-third of the freight handled by our railroads, and more than three-fourths of the traffic of some lines. Indeed, as a matter of fact, the number of miles of railroad track underground in the state of Pennsylvania is greater than that on the surface. An enormous activity in the transportation of coal goes on underground where the ordinary person never sees it, for the place in which it is being dug from its age-old home may be a mile or two from the point at which it finally appears on the surface.

Most people who live in the Eastern United States probably think of the anthracite, that is so familiar to them as a domestic fuel, when coal is mentioned. That is not what I have in mind, however, for anthracite constitutes only about one-eighth of all the coal this country produces, the rest of it being what is loosely referred to as "soft" coal. Perhaps that phrase evokes in the mind a picture of clouds of black smoke with a characteristic odor, but that also is an error.

Soft, or bituminous coal as it is more accurately termed, can be, and nearly all of it is, burned without producing any smoke. The locomotives and tug-boats that produce smoke so abundantly do so not because of any inherent quality of the coal but because of the equipment and procedure they employ. Smoke is like an accident, something that can be almost wholly prevented if people will only take the trouble to do it. The big power plants that generate steam and electricity burn their "soft" coal without any visible smoke, and within the past few years manufacturers have developed automatic stokers for house-heating boilers that are equally guiltless of the production of smoke.

Perhaps the most remarkable thing about bituminous coal is the very low cost at which it is produced; more than ten pounds for one cent is the usual price at which it sells at the mine. Transportation from the mine to the retail distributing yard costs as much, and frequently two or three times as much, as it costs to produce it. The retailer has to be recompensed for taking it to and putting it in the cellar, but even with all these added costs piled up against it bituminous coal seldom costs, even those who buy it only in small lots, more than a half-cent per pound. And since two pounds, properly utilized, will do the work of a man for a day it is the equivalent of being able to hire an able-bodied man for one cent per day. If that is not magic when our present wage scales are considered, what is?

Curiously enough, until recently all of the coal that works such wonders in replacing human labor on the surface had to be loaded with a hand shovel into the cars in which it is transported underground. Now mechanical devices for loading it are coming into extensive use. The reason why the improvement is not being made more rapidly is that often extensive changes in the layout underground first have to be made. If, however, you divide the total number of tons of coal produced by a mining company by the total number of men it employs you will usually find that, under present practice, the output corresponds to about five tons per man per day. As a ton of coal will do the work of a thousand men for a day coal mining is an occupation in which each man is doing the work of a regiment.

Judging by the wage controversies that we periodically hear about, coal miners do not seem, however, to be a group that earn very high wages. How does it happen that men doing such tremendously productive work do not earn enough to keep them always satisfied? The basic reason is that bituminous coal sells for less than $2 per ton at the mine. The average actual price in 1930 was $1.70 per ton, but that was computed by including the mines (23 per cent of all of them) that send their product to consuming companies that own them, and therefore have no incentive to make the price low. The coal sold in the open market undoubtedly received less than the average price. The output of a man for a day therefore sells for about $8 and, in many cases, sells for less. Not all of that sum can go to him in wages, for some of it must go to pay for the materials used, for power, the cost of haulage underground, the cost of hoisting, and of operating the fans and pumps that keep the mines free of gas and water, for the cost of preparation and sizing, and no inconsiderable fraction of it must go to pay taxes. The fraction remaining to pay wages to the coal miner can be, therefore, no large sum even if he got it every day in the year, and, unfortunately, he does not get it every day or even anything like it. The coal mines of the country in 1930 averaged 187 days work; in

Indiana they worked only 157 days that year. There have been times when the buying of coal was so fast and furious that all the mines were busy trying to produce it and there are other times when a majority of them are shut down. Now a coal mine is not like a factory that you just close and leave it alone, the fans and pumps must be kept going, inspection must be kept up and there are various other sources of expense, so that a moderate sized mine may be spending a thousand dollars a day in addition to its fixed or "overhead" charges without producing any coal at all. It is this irregularity, the small fraction of the year, due to over-capacity, on which the coal mines operate, and the low price at which they sell their product that are the basic reasons why operators and miners are unable to secure an adequate return for their work. That is why coal production is a relatively unlucrative business, but there are other reasons why this condition exists.

One of them was touched on in the preceding chapter, where it was said that our coal consumption doubled every ten years between 1870 and 1900, but between 1920 and 1930 did not increase at all. The coal industry instead of benefiting by progress has been, to some extent, the victim of it. During the earlier years the steadily increasing demand for heat and energy was met by increasing

the production and consumption of coal.   But in
the past quarter-century attention has increasingly
turned toward the securing of a higher degree of
efficiency in its utilization.   In ten years the
amount of work that a ton of coal can do was
doubled.   This happened in public utility plants
that burn coal to generate electricity for distribution through wires to consumers of light and power.
In 1902 to generate a kilowatt-hour of electricity
required 6.6 pounds of coal; by 1907 it was done
with 4 pounds, and in 1930 the public utility plants
used only 1.62 pounds, on the average.   Public
utilities continued to increase but the plants did
not correspondingly increase their coal consumption.

The railroads have always been the principal
customer of the bituminous coal mines, at one
time taking nearly one-third their output.   While
the railroads were not able to make so large an increase in the efficiency with which they use coal
as the public utilities have done, they also learned
between 1917 and 1927 how to haul a train a one-
third longer distance with the same quantity of
coal, and 50 per cent further increase seems possible.   On the other hand, increase of truck transportation has affected the total business done by
the railroads.

This leads to the next point, the competition of

substitute fuels. It is not simply that the truck,
propelled by gasoline, has taken over part of the
transportation function of the railroads, but the
rapidly increasing demand for gasoline has created
another threat to coal. From a barrel of crude
petroleum about one-third of a barrel of gasoline
is usually produced; more can be made, but only
at a higher cost. Among the other products from
a barrel of crude are kerosene and lubricating oils
that can be sold for normal uses; and there are
others, such as wax, asphalt, and petroleum coke
that meet demands. But a considerable quantity
of heavy residue fuel oil is thus made available for
uses in which it is in direct competition with coal.
Being liquid, it has an advantage for a variety of
purposes, as in fuel for ships. Many householders
heat their dwellings with fuel oil because the convenience of automatic control outweighs for them
an increased cost. Sometimes an actual saving
can be made. The owner of two adjacent apart-
ment houses, heated by coal, with a janitor for
each, put in oil heating and one man was able to
look after both plants. Thus in a variety of ways,
in spite of somewhat higher cost and the need for
special equipment, fuel oil was enabled to gain a
considerable market in competition with coal.

This is not all, however. The exploratory operations for crude oil supplies made available large

quantities of natural gas. At first this was used in field drilling, any other practicable way, or simply allowed to go to waste. In recent years, however, it has been learned that it is the expansive force of gas dissolved in the oil that brings the petroleum out of the ground, that much oil still remains after the gas has escaped, and that by control of the gas pressure the total quantity of oil obtained can be greatly increased. Consequently the gas is kept under careful control and this makes its recovery and use more practicable. Experience also indicated that the quantity of gas to be obtained was larger than had been supposed, and therefore more worth the expenditure of capital to recover and use it. Consequently natural gas that, except for a few places, had found little use save as a fuel in field operations or for the manufacture of carbon black, began to be recognized as a competitor with coal. It is this competition of other fuels as well as the greater efficiency in the use of coal that has checked the previous rate of growth of coal consumption.

The loss of a steadily increasing market has caused the producers of coal to seek other means of promoting the use of their commodity. One means has been to produce a higher-grade coal by freeing it of impurities. This had long been practiced with anthracite coal and also on bituminous coal that was to be used for making coke. The ordinary consumer did not at first pay any attention to the quantity or nature of the ash in the coal he bought. More careful study of his problems revealed that the ash often created difficulties in the use of the coal and producers undertook to remove it in order to compete with others whose coal was naturally of better quality. A variety of methods are used in the cleaning of coal, both wet and dry processes being applied. Each involves technical problems, that need not be discussed here, and also an additional cost that it is difficult to get consumers to meet through a willingness to pay an increased price for the cleaned coal. Where, however, the cleaning process distinctly improves the usefulness of the coal for a specific purpose, as contrasted to a mere reduction of its ash content, consumers are more easily convinced. It is evident, however, that this procedure is intended to help the producer who uses it to sell his own coal, and only incidentally promotes the use of coal in competition with other fuels.

A more significant avenue of progress is to attempt to make coal more useful to man than it is when burned raw as fuel. We have found that there are other ways in which it can serve many important needs. To discuss them in detail would require far more space than I have available, and what follows is therefore only an illustrative outline.

We ordinarily think of coal as a natural form in which carbon occurs, and consequently suppose it consists almost entirely of carbon. Good anthracite may, indeed, contain over 90 per cent carbon, but it also contains about 1.5 per cent each of hydrogen and oxygen and 1 per cent nitrogen. In bituminous coals the nitrogen content remains about the same (only rising above 2 per cent in exceptional instances) but the hydrogen and oxygen content greatly increases. The carbon content correspondingly decreases and may fall below 60 per cent. It is clear then that when we speak of anthracite as "hard" coal and bituminous as "soft" coal we are making the distinction on a quality that is relatively unimportant, thus deflecting attention from the more important matter of its actual chemical composition. Let us consider for a moment the practical significance of the latter.

How anthracite and bituminous coal come to differ so markedly in composition need not detain us here, beyond noting that scientists have studied it with great care and have published the results of their studies in great detail. It will be enough to say that the original material from which the coal was derived was vegetable matter and it depends on what the nature of the original material

was, and what has happened to it since it was first
formed, as to what kind of coal is to be found in a
given bed.   Taking the world as a whole, most of
the coal is of the kind called bituminous.   Perhaps
the best way to define that not very precise term
is to say that it contains an appreciable hydrogen
content and the hydrogen is combined with the
carbon.   If the coal is heated some of these hydrocarbons will come off in the form of gas and others
as liquids.   One way of practically analyzing coal
is to first dry it, then heat it to a standard temperature, and hold it there for a time.   The percentage
of its weight lost under this treatment is designated
as "volatile hydrocarbons."   In ordinary bituminous coal this portion amounts to one-third, or a
little more, of the total weight of the coal as mined.
The coal used for gas-making will contain about
40 per cent volatile and cannel coal (for which
there is little practical use except for burning in
grates) nearly 50 per cent.

From the standpoint of industry, therefore, bituminous coal is not simply coal but a substance
of rather variable composition, and with correspondingly variable characteristics.   So long as bituminous coal was simply burned on grates for the
production of heat this did not much matter, for it
was easy to make necessary changes in the technique of burning it.   It was not easy to burn it

without producing smoke, however, and before the end of the sixteenth century experiments had been made in Germany to see whether something could not be done to produce a smokeless fuel. Nothing much resulted and it was not until 150 years later, or a little over two centuries ago, that the processing of bituminous coal began, for a quite different reason. Iron had, until then, been made with charcoal as fuel, but as the demand for it increased it became evident that the available wood supply, in England, would set a limit to the growth of its production. Experimenters tried to make a substitute for charcoal out of bituminous coal by heating it. This drove off the volatile matter and left a spongy residue that, in some ways, was even better than charcoal for iron making, since it permitted the use of much larger furnaces.

For about a hundred years after 1710 the ironmakers were content to merely drive off the volatile matter, but meanwhile, toward the end of the century, other pioneers had begun to treat the coal in order to obtain gas from the volatile matter to burn for illuminating purposes. These two uses went on simultaneously for another half-century; one group treating the coal to get the spongy residue and wasting the volatile matter, the other treating it to obtain the volatile matter and burning the residue as a smokeless fuel. It was not until fifty years ago that the technology required was so developed that the coke required for iron-making was successfully made in ovens that saved and utilized the volatile material.   For a long time thereafter practical operators still asserted that coke made in the old-fashioned ovens was better, and it is only within the past 25 years that it has been generally admitted that the coke made in "by-product" ovens, as they are called, is equally satisfactory for iron-making.

The Great War was a potent factor in accelerating the recognition of the economy of by-product coking.   In 1913, less than a third of our coke was made in the by-product ovens, but by 1919 nearly two-thirds of it was so made, and by 1928 over 90 per cent.   The value of the coke produced here in 1929 was a little over 278 million dollars, while the value of the by-products sold was nearly 164 million dollars.   What are these by-products?

Gas is the principal one, both by volume and value.   About 11,000 cubic feet of gas is recovered per ton of coal charged into a coking oven.   More than half of it is sold to gas companies for city lighting and most of the rest of it to steel and other companies for furnace heating, the total value in 1929 being over 84 million dollars.   Next in importance is ammonia, a little over 22 pounds per ton of raw coal, making a total of over a billion and a half pounds in 1929, with a value of nearly 30 million dollars. And a little over 30 million dollars represents the value of the light oils and their derivatives that were also recovered from the apparently insignificant yield of a little less than 3 gallons per ton of raw coal. More than half of it was motor benzol, with toluol as the next ingredient of value. Solvent naptha and xylol are others of a great company of useful products derived from the crude.

Nearly nine gallons of tar per ton of coal is also obtained in coking, and the total produced in 1929 had a value of about 20 million dollars. Much of it is burned as a liquid fuel, but an amazing number of chemical compounds can be produced from it. Creosote, napththalene, and phenol are the most familiar of them. The statistics for 1929 read "phenol (crude), 78,869 gallons; value $28,-347" and from such a brief statement scarcely a hint of its real importance can be gained. Crude phenol is not only the raw material from which carbolic acid and such commercial products as lysol are obtained, but is also the material from which "condensation products," such as bakelite and redmanol, are obtained.

That part of the tar sold which is not simply burned but is used as the raw material of chemical processes is the beginning of endless wonders.

The simplest way to represent it is as a tree, with tar as the trunk and all the hundreds of derived products, such as drugs and dyes, as twigs on the ends of the branches. Few of those who use these materials think of them as mineral substances, yet they have their origin in coal. We can not here go further into this matter, but enough has perhaps been said to make it clear that most of the progress of the past century in commercial chemistry has its origin in the mineral industry. Interested persons should read the chapters on coal tar colors and synthetic perfumes and flavors in E. E. Slosson's "Creative Chemistry."

Another question that immediately arises is a quantitative one. We produce and consume about half a billion tons of bituminous coal yearly, of which about 75 million tons is converted into coke, producing by-products that are worth more than half as much of the coke, while the coke is worth more than the raw coal charged. The question immediately arises why not coke all the coal? Is it not a waste to burn most of it simply as raw coal? To answer the question adequately would require too much discussion of technical detail. A simple answer is to say that the amount of coke now made is enough to supply the present demand for coke, and that the tar, for example, is more than enough to meet the existing need for coal tar products, so that much of it is simply burned as liquid fuel.

That immediately raises another question, why burn coal raw; why not burn coke, thus permitting the recovery of the by-products. That question is even more difficult to answer in a simple way. Only part of the bituminous coal produced yearly is capable of being made into good coke, of the quality needed for iron-blast furnaces and other consumers. By mixing different grades of coal and by admitting that for many possible purposes the best quality of coke is not essential, the amount of coal that might be coked is greatly increased. Many people believe this is quite practicable, but the results of experience so far are discouraging. Theoretically it should be possible, in a large city, to sell the gas thus produced to the gas company, sell the coke for house-heating purposes, and utilize the by-products. To sell the gas is not difficult, but to market the coke is not easy, and the management of the by-products is most difficult of all. What is known as the low-temperature coking process yields by-products that are not only different in amount but also in composition, and the best indication that we do not yet know how to turn all our coal supply into coke and save the valuable by-products is that it is not being done, although many brilliant minds have been at work on the problem for a long time.

The primitive magician was popularly supposed to know all that could be known and his powers were conceived to be unlimited. But in characterizing as modern magic the degree of control so far acquired over the ability of coal to serve the purposes of men we can claim no such omnipotence or omniscience. When using coal simply as a source of power best modern practice is able to utilize less than one-third of its available energy, and average practice probably not as much as one-fifth. Of its possible by-products only an insignificant fraction are yet being utilized, and it is comforting to reflect that since we have available, in this country, enough coal to last us at least a thousand years, and perhaps much longer, there is time to acquire the knowledge of how to use it more efficiently. And in justly being proud of the progress that has been made, let us couple it with a humble recognition of the possibility that our descendants may look back on what we have done with the same tolerance of our limitations that we display toward the technology of the seventeenth century.

CHAPTER III

THE MAGIC CARPET

Fʀᴏᴍ the beginning of time to the nineteenth century man never discovered any way to move from place to place at a much faster rate or to traverse a greater distance in a day than he could unaided. The potentate who made his slaves carry him saved himself exertion but he did not travel faster, nor farther in a day, than he could have progressed on his own two legs. Training animals to carry him served the same indolent purpose and enabled him to go a little faster and farther but not much. The Marathon is a distance of a little over 26 miles (26.218 miles) but a runner in 1930 covered it in less than $2\frac{1}{2}$ hours while another man ran 21 miles in less than two hours. Primitive men could probably have done nearly as well and horses not much better. Birds move swiftly, but man was never able to devise a way to make them carry him. So he dreamed of a magic carpet that would instantaneously take him from where he was to where he wanted to be.

In justice to early men it should be observed

that they did make one major invention in the field of transportation by building ships and devising sails to force the wind to move them. Thus they were enabled to travel on the water at a good speed and, what was more important, to traverse distances that were quite beyond their natural powers. But aside from that man's ability to move himself and his possessions about was not greatly increased until the development of the steam engine made the railroad a possibility. Railroads are a characteristic example of how minerals multiply the powers of men, for they are almost wholly constructed of minerals, and the power to operate them is derived from minerals. They were soon so developed that they could transport men at three or four times the previous speed for short distances, and enabled him to travel ten times as far in a day as he previously could.

This was a great advance, but it still did not meet man's desires. It was a reasonable approximation to the magic carpet if a man wanted to follow the route of the railroad train and to go when it started, but he could not go alone, at any desired time, to any desired place. He needed something that was more directly under his personal control. He acquired the railroad at the beginning of our century of progress, but much of the hundred years had elapsed before he found another avenue of progress through the utilization of another mineral, petroleum.

To primitive men petroleum was an object of curiosity but hardly much more, for they did not know how to use it. It came oozing to the surface of the earth and evaporated to a sticky water-resistant residue that Noah, in the legend of the Flood, was said to have used to make his Ark water-tight. Certainly they used it as a cement between bricks, for the ruins of their structures are still visible. In the rare instances where the natural substance was of such a quality as to permit its being burned in their lamps they used it, but it was never very satisfactory; it smoked, smelled, and was prone to explode. That is because it is a mixture of related substances that range from gases to solids, and they did not know how to separate it into fractions.

That knowledge, as often happens, came by transfer from another field. The people who had been using coal to make gas to burn found they could also make from it a liquid, oil, which could be burned in lamps quite as well as the animal and vegetable oils that they had been using for thousands of years. They had to change the design of the lamps, but that they could and did do.

Then, by one of those sudden syntheses of exist-

ing knowledge that sometimes happens, a new industry was created with dramatic completeness.
Men had long been drilling wells deep in the earth
to obtain water, both fresh and salt. The Chinese
drilled wells over 3000 feet deep to obtain salt water
for salt-making in the middle ages. The wells in
this country were shallower because we were able
to obtain it nearer the surface. Petroleum and
gas often came out of these wells, usually to the
disgust of the drillers, though the thrifty Chinese
used the gas to evaporate the brine.

When it became clear that a satisfactory oil for
burning could be made from petroleum a salt-well
driller was hired, in 1859, to put down a well at
Titusville, Pennsylvania, that yielded only crude
petroleum. In August, 1859, crude petroleum
sold for $80 per barrel of 42 gallons, in December
for a quarter of that, and by 1861 it was offered in
the Titusville region for 10 cents per barrel at the
well, since it was being produced faster than it
could be transported or sold. In 1930 in the new
field in East Texas it was again being offered for
10 cents per barrel, for the same reason. In the
seventy-year period there have been brief temporary shortages but typically there has been an
over-supply. In the past two years some 80 million more barrels have been used than has been
produced, but that is because the wells are throt-

tled down, and we could produce it at twice the rate we are using it.

In 1861 the production of crude petroleum in the United States was over 2,000,000 barrels and in 1871 over 5,000,000. By 1881 it had reached almost 28,000,000, and by 1891 over 54,000,000. In the first and third decades the output doubled, but in the second intermediate decade it quintupled. In that period the transportation and refining of the crude was changed from a chaos of disorganization into a well-managed industry under such centralized control that it lead to much public clamor later on. That story has been told elsewhere, what concerns us here is that during all this period petroleum was produced for the purpose of making kerosene, for burning in lamps. The crude from Pennsylvania also yielded a considerable fraction of lubricating oil that was also valuable. The lighter fractions, now called gasoline, then had no use of any importance; the refiners put as much into the kerosene as safety and regulations would permit and the rest was burned, often in open pits, to dispose of it.

Unknown to the producers of petroleum, developments that were of the greatest importance to them had begun. The need for a mechanical means of transportation more flexible than railroads, existing from the beginning, had lead to work here and there that, in spite of discouragements, was slowly but steadily making important progress in overcoming the many difficulties. Most of the early work was based on the idea of using a steam engine as the source of power, but experimenters were also working on the idea of using the explosive force of hydrocarbon gas or vapor, mixed with air, instead of the expansive force of steam, to operate an engine.   In 1876 Otto devised a successful four-cylinder gas engine, and in 1883 Daimler made the first high-speed internal-combustion engine using gasoline as fuel.   That success made possible its incorporation in the "horseless carriage" design.

The year 1894 marks another sudden synthesis of a large amount of previous work.   Haynes operated the first successful automobile in America. Four automobiles were built here the next year; in 1905 over 24,000 were built and the number then in operation was over 77,000.   Some of these were operated by steam, or electric storage batteries, but it early became evident that the internal combustion engine, using gasoline as a fuel, had such practical advantages that it would dominate this field.   Gasoline soon shifted from a troublesome by-product of the petroleum industry into being its most important product.   By 1919 there were over 7,500,000 automobiles registered in the United

States and our domestic consumption of gasoline reached 88,648,000 barrels of 42 gallons each. By 1930 the automobile registration had passed 26,-500,000 and the gasoline consumption was 398,-075,000 barrels. Crude petroleum production slightly exceeded a billion barrels in the United States in 1929. The gasoline now produced is more than four times as much as the kerosene in quantity.

But let us not get lost in a forest of statistics. The simple fact is that there are now enough automobiles in the United States so that every person in the country could simultaneously set out for any point that the four or five persons in each vehicle could agree upon. At the normal speed at which they would travel they would go as far in an hour as people could in a day a century earlier. The magic carpet is not quite yet an actuality, but man's ability to go anywhere at any time he wants to has been immensely multiplied. The essentially mineral aggregate that we call an automobile can travel much faster than indicated, for speed records of as high as 246 miles per hour have been made under special conditions for a single mile, while railroad trains have averaged over 80 miles per hour for more than a hundred miles.

An even nearer approach to the magic carpet in speed is the airplane, another outgrowth of the development of the internal combustion engine. To fly through the air has been one of man's ambitions ever since the days of the legendary Daedelus and Icarus. The first idea, that it could be done with mechanically-operated flapping wings, was baseless, but when the right way, of forcing an inclined surface through the air at high speed, was hit upon, the problem was to construct an engine and accessories able to do more than lift its own weight. Many experts thought it impossible, and it would have been without a light internal combustion engine using a fuel with a high energy content per pound of weight.

In 1903 Wilbur Wright made the first successful flight, at Kittyhawk, N. C., and by the outbreak of the Great War in 1914 the airplane had been so perfected that it was one of the most important military weapons. By the end of 1931 there were air services in regular operation over 31,783 miles of airways within the United States, and lines to points outside bringing the total to nearly 51,000 miles; on many of the lines more than one company was operating. In the air races of 1930 speeds of from 150 to 200 miles per hour were recorded and Frank M. Hawks flew from Havana to New York, about 1400 miles, at an average rate of 190 miles per hour. The fastest journey around the world, made by an airplane in 1931, required 8 days 15 hours and 51 minutes of elapsed time, of which 106 hours and 8 minutes was spent in flying, at an average rate of nearly 150 miles per hour.

Everything considered, the automobile is perhaps the nearest approximation to a magic carpet, for it is a personal possession, which can be used for transport from where you are to where you want to go, at any time, and is almost independent of weather conditions. The airplanes, like trains, must start from a special place and stop at another, though they are low enough in cost so an individual can own them. Even that does not permit him to go wherever and whenever he wishes, for it is difficult to fly with safety after dark and even in the daytime unfavorable weather is so a great a handicap as to make flying inadvisable. But when we compare what has been done in the past fifty years with the progress of all time that went before no one would venture to prophesy that we have approached as closely to the dream as is practicable.

Since we have been discussing the rôle of petroleum in making it possible for men to do what they want, some of its less dramatic services should be mentioned. The most useful and the least dramatic is as a lubricant for the moving parts of machinery. It has almost a monopoly of that service, and the range of its capabilities extends from the balance wheel of a watch to huge rotors that weigh tons. The reason for this is that it has the power of insinuating itself between two closely-fitting metal surfaces, so that when they move they rub on the oil instead of on each other. This not only reduces the wear but also the power required to move them. Every automobile owner knows how important good lubrication is to his machine, and that it needs different kinds of lubrication in different places. Perhaps he has sometimes burned out a bearing and thus knows how expensive it can be to repair the damage done when lubrication fails. The old rhyme says "You never miss the water till the well runs dry" and a modern paraphrase might be that you never think much about lubricating oil till the bearing runs dry.

Lubricating oil to the exent of over thirty-four million barrels was produced in the United States in 1930; of an average value, at the refinery, of about $8 per barrel, or $2\frac{1}{2}$ times the value of gasoline. Gasoline production, the same year, was 436,217,000 barrels. It would be useless to argue which is the more important, for both are essential in our modern mineral civilization.

Fuel oil is another petroleum product that has recently come to be important. Some crude petroleums, when separated into fractions, yield gasoline, kerosene, lubricating oil, and paraffine wax. But almost all natural petroleum contains some heavy dark asphaltic material; the "paraffin-base" oils are those in which the asphalt content is small. In some cases it is quite large in amount, and after the refiner has taken off the light fractions by distillation, he has left a quantity of tarry-looking liquid for which there was, at first, no use. Now he can either "crack" it into lighter fractions or sell it as fuel oil.

Before discussing fuel oil a word must be said about cracking. Twenty-five years ago a 42-gallon barrel of crude oil yielded only about $4\frac{1}{2}$ gallons of gasoline by distillation and the rapidly growing demand for that fraction made it urgent to find some way of increasing the yield. It was noticed that the gases issuing from the wells with the oil carried gasoline vapor, like fog, and a way was soon found of recovering it by absorption or compression. The first gasoline recovered in this way was in 1911 and in 1929 the quantity thus obtained was 2,233,688,000 gallons, an important addition to our supply. About the same time it became evident from laboratory experiments, that if the viscous asphaltic fraction of natural gasoline were subjected to heat and pressure it could be "cracked" into lighter substances, just as though someone were able to find a way to transmute

tough bull-beef into tender veal. In 1919 the
average barrel of crude was yielding almost eleven
gallons of gasoline, and in 1930 the return was 17.4
gallons. (It might be added that in 1909 the yield
of kerosene was almost 14 gallons per barrel of
crude, and in 1930 only a little more than 2).

This new process was almost too successful. It
was eventually found that the gasoline made in
this way is even better for use in automobiles than
"straight-run" gasoline; it has better anti-knock
qualities, which is a technical way of saying that
it is less subject to premature ignition when highly
compressed. Modern automobiles use a higher
degree of compression than the earlier ones. But
it was also slightly more expensive, consequently
only so much of the heavy oil was cracked as was
necessary to meet the total demand.

Another way of increasing our output of gasoline
is through the hydrogenation process. With the
use of pressure, heat, and a suitable catalyst, hydrogen can be caused to combine with hydrocarbons.
The process is a general one and liquid vegetable
oils can, for example, be thus converted into solids,
like tallow. "Shortening" thus made is a familiar
material in almost every kitchen and the process
is of great importance in the food industry. Under
proper control a mixture of coal and heavy petroleum can be converted into gasoline by catalytic

hydrogenation, and some recent work indicates that as much as 80 per cent of the bituminous material can be turned into gasoline. When practically perfected the process will permit the refiner to turn out products of any desired quality in the desired relative amounts. Its use at present is hampered by the high cost of producing hydrogen; synthetic ammonia may solve the problem. It has been prophesied that coal can be turned into gas and then, by successive additions of hydrogen to the gas, synthetic fats, proteins, and dye-stuffs can be made; artificial silk may eventually be made by this process.

Meanwhile people had been experimenting with the possibility of using heavy oils, instead of gasoline, for power purposes. One thing that resulted was the Diesel engine, which uses heavy oil, forced into the cylinders at high pressure. This is the most efficient heat engine man has yet built; that is, it turns into work a larger proportion of the energy in the fuel (30 to 35 per cent), but it needs special equipment to start it, has only recently been successfully made in small sizes, and is a rather expensive mechanism to construct, though very economical in its use of fuel. It has proved to be very desirable for operating ships and for other uses where the power unit can be large and avoiding the explosion hazard of gasoline is important, but these characteristics have so far limited its use.

Until now the principal use for heavy oil has been to burn it as a liquid fuel. This brought it into competition with coal, where it proved to have some advantages A ton of heavy oil has a little more than twice the energy content of a ton of average coal, and its liquid form makes it possible to devise equipment that will feed it into the combustion chamber of a steam boiler without hand labor and with effective automatic control. The *Europa* and *Bremen*, the world's largest and fastest ships, burn fuel oil under steam boilers.

Ships and locomotives, where storage space for fuel supply is valuable, found this quality useful, and when small-sized equipment was made available many people began to use it for house heating, finding its convenience enough to compensate them for an increased fuel cost. Quantatively this latter is not a very important use, however, as some comparative figures will show.

In 1930 a little over 348 million barrels of fuel oil was consumed. The oil companies themselves used some 53 million barrels of this, and the steamships, the principal users, over 94 million barrels. The railroads used almost 68 million barrels and gas and electric power plants over 27 million. Two different uses are combined in the latter item, for the electric power plants used it to generate power, while the gas plants used it to increase the calorific power of the gas they make; about two-thirds of the total was used for this last purpose. Commercial heating (that is, for buildings other then dwellings) required over 17 million barrels, while iron and steel products used more than 15 million and other manufacturing almost 12 million barrels. Domestic heating took only 9,822,-000 barrels, or the heat equivalent of about $2\frac{1}{2}$ million tons of coal. The use of twice as much heavy oil in gas-making as in house-heating illustrates that the use of a mineral substance most familiar to the average man often is only one of its minor uses; it may be serving him in ways much more important, but of which he is only vaguely conscious.

A curious feature of the petroleum industry is the so-called law of capture. The owner of a fraction of the earth's surface owns everything beneath it. If solid minerals lie beneath they remain where they are until he gets ready to remove them. But oil and gas move through the strata, and may all escape through wells on adjoining land. Confronted with this fact, learned judges ruled that they were legally similar to wild game, which belongs to the man on whose land it was captured, no matter where it originally came from. This has created a great variety of technical, industrial, and social problems. Practically it means that if your neighbor begins producing petroleum you must produce too, else he will take yours along with his own. It also makes it difficult to shut down wells when production begins to run ahead of consumption. Much progress has recently been made toward establishing the legal right of common ownership in the underground pool.

It would be tiresome to attempt to go into many details, but enough has been said to indicate that the wish for a magic carpet has not only brought satisfaction of human desires but has multiplied human problems. The academic gentleman who thought that modern civilization was making life so easy that good minds would hereafter have little to occupy them was as mistaken as the man who resigned from the Patent Office many years ago, giving as his reason that everything that could possibly be invented had already been patented.

Perhaps some reader will have been thinking "What shall we do if our supply of crude petroleum gives out? No one can possibly know how much there is until it has been discovered, and perhaps some day when we look for it there will not be any more. Will our automobiles and airplanes some day become useless?"

In trying to answer this natural question it can

be said that there are parts of the earth where petroleum has not been found that may prove to be a source of it.   We now drill wells ten thousand feet deep in some places, and the use of deeper wells in others may increase the supply, though that is disputed.   Probably not more than a third or one-quarter of the oil actually in the earth now comes out of the wells, and much progress has been made in the last few years in increasing the proportion we can recover.   A little over a third of the crude produced is converted into gasoline; we can turn two-thirds of it into gasoline if we have to. About one-tenth of the energy in gasoline is converted into useful work in present practice; who would dare say that we cannot do better than that?

There is also the possibility that we can, at a price, derive gasoline from "oil" shales, that are something like the material from which petroleum has probably been derived by natural processes, which exist in considerable amount in the earth's crust.   And, finally, we can, and people do, in Germany, make gasoline from coal, though not cheaply enough to compete with gasoline made from petroleum at present price levels.   So the automobile owner can feel pretty confident that the only way in which his car will become useless is by wearing it out.

CHAPTER IV

THE SKELETON OF MODERN INDUSTRY

 The skeleton that supports the human body derives its strength from a mineral substance, calcium phosphate. The skeleton of modern industry is also a mineral substance, iron. When iron is alloyed with carbon, (and most of it is so alloyed) we call it steel, but to avoid the awkwardness of continually saying iron and steel the word "iron" here will frequently be used to include them both. Pure iron is too soft to be of much use to men. Although iron-bearing minerals occur more abundantly than those of any other metal (except aluminum) and iron is easily produced from them, it was not much used until long after other metals, especially copper and its alloys. One reason was that it took men a long while to learn how to control the carbon content of iron. Another reason is that it was not until engines began to be built, and more especially after railroads began to be constructed, that men had any large need for iron. It would be as profitless as the discussion which came first, the chicken or the egg, to consider whether the growing ability to produce iron brought about its increased use, or whether it was the other way around, but we can at least say that the period since the development of steam power has been the period of ascendancy of iron. Coal and iron are a naturally associated couple, like ham and eggs or Mutt and Jeff.

The making of iron was well established in the United States a hundred years ago, for the method of making and rolling wrought (soft, pure) iron, devised by Cort in England some thirty years earlier, had been introduced here in 1817. The use of coke as fuel in the blast furnace, successfully practiced in England for more than a hundred years, was not introduced here till 1840, however. The reason, of course, was that wood for making charcoal was so much more abundant here, and it had also been found that anthracite coal could be used. For a time technologists thought it equally desirable and it was not until 1875 that more pig iron was made with coke as fuel than with anthracite. It was only in 1869, indeed, that coke exceeded charcoal as the fuel for making pig iron.

Meanwhile two other important things had happened. Iron ore from the Lake Superior district, that now supplies seven eighths of our raw mineral for iron making, was first used in 1853, ten years after it was discovered. Not until 1871 did the production of ore from that region reach a million tons yearly, but it was destined to reshape the structure of our iron industry. The second was the making of steel by the Bessemer process, at Troy, N. Y., in 1865. Ten years later 375,000 tons of steel were made by that process in a single year.

We must go back to the making of iron from its ores to understand what that development meant. Iron is found all over the earth in the form of iron oxide and the metal can be made from the oxide by heating it with carbon; you can do it yourself by burying some lumps of ore in the fuel bed of your house-heating furnace. That will produce soft iron, with the impurities that were in the ore embedded in the iron. By hammering it while it is hot they can be gotten rid of fairly well, and a skilful person can hammer the iron into almost any desired shape. The difficulty is that it remains soft, too soft to be of much practical use. Nor can it be melted down and cast, for the melting point of pure iron, around 2700°F., was far above the reach of the early metallurgists.

The early workers were clever, however, and they eventually found out how to harden iron. They made the soft metal, worked it by hammering into the shape desired, heated it for a while buried in carbon, and then took it out and plunged

it into water or oil.   If they did it just right they
could make it as hard as a modern razor blade.
Of course they did not know why it happened nor
did they need to, so long as they could do it.   Now
we understand that the carbon of the fuel bed
slowly soaks into the hot iron, much as moisture
soaks into wood.   Iron with carbon dissolved in
it has the property of becoming hard when chilled
from a red heat; less than a quarter of a per cent
of carbon is enough to produce an increase in hardness that is perceptible by even crude tests.   There
is no need of going above 1.5 per cent carbon, for
above 1 per cent the steel begins to become brittle
as well as hard.   Since the carbon soaked in from
the outside a skilful smith could make a sword with
a hard edge and a tough body that was an excellent
weapon.   They could make good steel, but they
could not make it in large quantities and it was
quite expensive.

Meanwhile the early metallurgists had learned
how to melt iron.   If they used a blast and increased the depth of the fuel bed they could produce
melted metal, though it hardly seemed like iron,
for when it was cold it was as brittle as glass.
They could cast it, however, and much of the iron
used before 1750 was cast iron.   We know now
that when made in this way the iron takes up as
as much as 3.5 per cent carbon and its melting

point is lowered some 500°F., though still far above that of bronze. At the beginning of our century of progress this kind of iron was still universally made in furnaces that had a capacity of six tons per day. The remains of them can still be seen at many places throughout the eastern United States, especially in Pennsylvania.

A half-century earlier Cort had found how to convert this brittle iron into the pure, soft variety and how to roll, instead of hammer, the soft iron into bars and strips. A hundred years ago both hard and soft iron could be made by the ton, and that must have seemed a wonderful advance to those who knew how it had originally been made, a few pounds at a time, with infinite labor. But steel was still made from the soft iron and only on a small scale.

What Bessemer learned to do, in 1856, was to produce steel from the melted hard iron by blowing air through it; in 20 minutes he could convert 15 tons of the hard, brittle metal into steel soft enough to be rolled, yet much stronger than the pure soft iron. Now it was possible to produce the kind of metal needed for building railroads, in large quantities and at a low price. The process was introduced in this country in 1865. The total iron production of the country in 1864 was about a million tons; ten years later it was more than

$2\frac{1}{2}$ million tons and twenty years later about 5 million tons. Sixty years later it was about forty million tons.[1]

For many years after its introduction the Bessemer process was the principal way of making steel. Contemporaneous with it was another process, known as the open-hearth, that at first seemed less advantageous, since it required more fuel and had less capacity. Gradually it was improved and then turned out to have advantages, for it could use metal higher in phosphorus than the Bessemer process. Ore that was low enough in phosphorus to be suitable for the Bessemer process was not common, and brought a premium price. This other process could not only handle metal made from any kind of ore, but the steel was of better quality. By 1907 more steel was made by the open-hearth process than by the Bessemer, and by 1929 seven times as much.

So far we have spoken only of the making of iron and its carbon alloys, cast iron and steel, and have seen that progress consisted chiefly in learning how to make them in larger quantities, more cheaply,

[1] Statistics of iron and steel production are confusing because much steel is produced by re-melting old iron and steel. Thus over 56 million tons of steel was produced in 1929, though only 42 million tons of pig iron was made from ore, and about one-third of it was not made into steel.

and of better quality. But all the time experimenters were working with alloys of other substances with iron. In the production of steel by the Bessemer process a manganese alloy was used, and while the manganese did not stay with the iron the need of the modern mind to understand why things happen lead to careful study and precise measurements that immensely speeded up the process of finding how to make new combinations.

One of the things thus learned was that nickel, chromium, tungsten, and some other metals, if added to steel, make it stronger without making it brittle, as carbon does. Long, careful, and painstaking work was needed, because the effects produced by different amounts are surprisingly different, and it also makes a great deal of difference how the steel is treated.

With nickel, for example, less than 2 per cent does very little good, but by using between 2 and 4 per cent the tensile strength of the steel is increased about 6000 pounds per square inch for each per cent of nickel added, it is also more resistant to rusting and abrasion. If more nickel is added the alloy becomes too hard to be easily worked, but is useful for special purposes. Above 10 per cent nickel the steel, instead of getting harder when heated and chilled, gets softer. Steel containing 13 per cent nickel is tremendously strong, but so hard it cannot be cut or drilled. At 24 per cent nickel the alloy becomes non-magnetic, and from that up to 32 per cent it has a high resistance to the passage of the electric current. The wire coils in the toaster, now a feature of every breakfast table are usually an alloy of nickel and chromium, however, not an iron-nickel alloy.

At 36 per cent nickel the alloy developes another curious property; it does not expand and contract with changes in the temperature, fitting it for special uses, such as measuring tapes. The wires that lead in through the glass of an electric light bulb are made from a 38 per cent nickel-iron alloy plated with copper. They expand and contract at the same rate as the glass and consequently do not crack away from it. At 78 per cent nickel its magnetic permeability becomes exceedingly high, and this discovery has revolutionized the making of cables for the transmission of messages under the sea. A concrete illustration of the practical importance of such special qualities is seen in a recent estimate that the electrical transformers now in use in the United States waste about ten billion kilowatt-hours of energy annually in useless heat. Half of this could be saved if the nickel-iron alloy (50 per cent) which has the combination of highest permeability and lowest hysteresis loss were used in their construction.

Chromium makes steel hard. Files contain about 0.5 per cent of it, axes and hammers and chains up to nearly 1 per cent. Balls and rollers for bearings are probably the most important use for chromium steel. For many uses chromium and nickel are both added, for when their good effects were learned, some fifty years ago, it was soon noted that for many purposes it was better to use both than only one. A ratio of 2 to $2\frac{1}{2}$ times as much nickel as chromium seems to be most satisfactory. Armor plate for battle-ships, which typically has about 4 per cent nickel and 2 per cent chromium, is an important use, but the nickel-chromium steels that enter most directly into the lives of ordinary people are those employed in motor-car building.

An automobile is, indeed, an excellent example of the great number of varieties of iron required in modern construction. Most of the visible outside parts are made of iron sheets, and so a metal that is easily rolled is needed. It is made like steel, but is so low in carbon as to be almost pure iron. The main mass of the engine has to be cast, and consequently material containing several per cent of carbon is used. The frame needs to be light and strong, and able to resist shock, but must be built up of sections that are produced by rolling. Different qualities are used, according to the price of the car; the cheaper cars employ a steel with enough carbon to give it strength and stiffness, the more costly ones use more expensive alloys that provide greater strength and resistance to shock. Many parts of the mechanism have to be forged and must be of a quality that permits that operation. The front axle must be strong and tough, and so will usually contain nickel; the hardness necessary in the bearings will be provided by chromium, and so on.

Formerly motor cars were trimmed with nickel-plated iron. Recently chromium plating has been substituted for nickel, for although it is more costly it resists tarnishing better. Some of the cheaper cars have substituted an iron-nickel-chromium alloy that is highly resistant to tarnish and almost silver-white in color. This belongs to the group of alloys, of recent devising, that are popularly known by the somewhat ungrammatical name of stainless steel. The various companies that produce this material apply different trade names to it; but the material always contains about 18 per cent chromium and 8 per cent nickel. Since nickel costs about twenty and chromium almost fifty times as much as iron to produce, the raw material for this alloy is relatively expensive and the fact that its ability to resist tarnish depends somewhat on a highly-finished surface also adds to its cost. But its attractive appearance and freedom from the cost of subsequent polishing, or of need for protective coatings, has lead to its wide use. Several of the larger office buildings in New York City have used it extensively for outside metal work as well as for indoor construction. The newest member of the iron alloy family, it has quickly taken a leading rôle, and alloys of this type offer the most promise of significant future development.

Corrosion, or "rust," has always been the great enemy of iron. The pure, or "wrought" iron was fairly rust resistant, but both steel and cast iron were much attacked by the combined action of air and moisture. Painting the surface was a common means of protection, and the painting operations so often noticed on bridges and other structures are for protection rather than for appearance sake. For many uses steel can be protected by dipping it in melted tin or zinc, and for others it is plated with nickel or chromium. These recent developments have not only produced a metal that is truly resistant to corrosion (there are also rustless cast irons) but have lead to the production of special alloys having a remarkable resistance to the attack of almost any reagent, including strong acids.

An important alloy that has not yet been mentioned is that with tungsten. That metal when mixed with iron not only makes a hard steel but one that stays hard even when red hot, when all other varieties of steel soften. Modern boring and cutting machines were previously limited in speed by ability to keep the tool cool, as it gets hot when working and as soon as it heats up loses its edge. A great deal of work, done over a long period of years, has disclosed that about 18 per cent tungsten with 3.5 per cent chromium gives the best results, permitting cutting operations to go on at six times the rate of an ordinary carbon steel. Tungsten is also a useful addition in the steel of which magnets, so essential in many electrical devices, are made.

Manganese as an addition to steel must also be mentioned, but as it is discussed in detail in Chapter IX, we will pass over it for the moment.

Vanadium and molybdenum are two other metals that improve steel quality. Vanadium produces much the same effect as nickel, but a much smaller amount is required. Chrome-vanadium steels are used in an important way in the driving axles and other forgings of locomotives, automobile springs and axles, gun forgings and many other purposes. Molybdenum-vanadium steels have proved valuable for making centrifugally cast guns. Modern advertising has made molybdenum steel familiar to the general public, but its use as yet is not extensive, being about one-half million tons yearly. There are many others, such as zirconium and beryllium, whose effects on steel are being actively studied, but to refer to them all would not only spin this tale out too long, but would also jumble, in a confusing way, things that are important and interesting, but used very little, with the things that chiefly compose the skeleton of the modern industry. To restore our sense of proportion let us resurvey the field before leaving it.

At the beginning of our century of progress iron workers knew how to make the iron-carbon alloy called pig iron from ore, and how to use it in making castings. The furnaces were of small capacity, but so little metal per capita was then needed that that was all right. From pig iron they could make the pure iron called wrought iron, and steel from wrought iron. The processes were difficult and laborious, and could turn out only small quantities. The first part of the century was marked by quantitative development. Pig iron furnaces increased in size and speed from ten tons daily output to a thousand at present. One modern blast furnace can furnish more metal than the whole country produced a century earlier. The annual requirement of new metal per capita at the beginning of the period was less than 17 pounds, now it is 1000. Most of it at the beginning of the period was cast and wrought iron, now most of it is steel.

The improvements in steel-making processes we have described brought about this shift of emphasis as well as increase in quantity. Fifty years ago steel could be made so cheaply in large quantity that subsequent development was toward improving its quality and fitting it for special uses by the development of special combinations of qualities. The last quarter century might be called the beginning of the age of alloy steel. The great uses for steel, however, that absorb most of the total produced, are met by ordinary steel.

In 1929 some $42\frac{1}{2}$ million tons of new iron, made from ore, were produced. Over $41\frac{1}{2}$ million tons were the ordinary iron-carbon alloy, pig-iron, but a little over 850,000 tons were special iron alloys, chiefly iron-silicon and iron-manganese, used in steel making. A little less than one-quarter of the pig iron was used as cast iron, and in other ways, and the remainder was turned into steel. In other words, a little over 30 million tons of pig iron were available for steel making. From this about $56\frac{1}{2}$ million tons of steel were made. The difference was, of course, made up by remelting old iron and steel. Over 48 million tons were made by the open-hearth process, 7 million by the Bessemer and 6645 tons by the crucible process, in which wrought iron or low carbon steel is converted into steel of specially high quality. The wrought iron, used for pipe and other purposes, was also produced from pig iron. No statistics are available as to the quantity made, but it did not much exceed 450,000 tons, for low-carbon steel meets many of the uses once served by wrought iron.

Of the 56 million tons of steel produced over 40 million tons were rolled into shapes and sold. These were as follows: bars, 19 per cent; sheets, 15 per cent; shapes, (beams, etc.) 11.5 per cent; pipe, 11 per cent; plates, 11 per cent; wire, 7 per cent; rails, 7 per cent; strips, 6 per cent; tin plate, 5 per cent. This rolled steel was used in different industries, as follows: automotive, 18 per cent; railroads, 17 per cent; building and construction, 16.5 per cent; oil, gas, water, and mining, 10.5 per cent; exports, 5.5 per cent; agriculture, 5.5 per cent; containers, 5 per cent; machinery, 3 per cent. It is interesting to note that the railroads are still one of the principal users of steel and still more surprising to find that they take six times as much of it as goes into machinery manufacture.

It is evident, too, from this tabulation that most of our requirements for steel are met by what is known in the trade as mild steel, a material low in carbon and practically without important alloy addition. The steel industry is something like a bakery that sells a great variety of cakes and pies at relatively high prices but devotes most of its productive capacity to bread, which is sold cheap.

New steel produced yearly amounts, in this country, to about 1000 pounds per person, a little over half of it derived from new iron and the rest from old material. This compares with about 20 pounds per person a hundred years earlier, not of steel but almost wholly of cast iron and wrought iron. No statistics are available as to the quantities of alloy steels that we now use, and perhaps it is just as well, for their importance in modern life is far beyond their quantitative importance.

CHAPTER V

VULCAN'S THREE SONS

Modern life requires more iron and steel than of all the other metals combined and multiplied many times. The world's requirement of iron is about a hundred million tons yearly, while no other metal amounts to as much as ten million. There are, indeed, only three metals of which the world's yearly output exceeds a million tons; these are copper, lead, and zinc. Copper and lead go back to the earliest ages of mankind in service to him, but zinc is distinctly modern. It has only been used since Roman times and was not produced as a separate metal for more than a thousand years later. Preparatory to considering the parts these three metals play in modern life, it will be well to review their history.

Copper is frequently found as a metal in nature, but it is too soft to be of much use, for it is no harder than gold. It is so much more abundant, occurs in larger pieces, and is as easily worked as gold, so it was early made into ornaments and vessels. It can easily be reduced from its ores and the copper made in this way is harder, for almost any other substance in copper hardens it and many of them lower its melting point. Tin is especially helpful in this way, and the resulting metal is not only harder but its hardness can be further increased by hammering. Until men learned how to control the carbon content of iron the copper-tin alloy called bronze was the best material men had to make axes, swords, and knives. At first it was made by smelting natural mixtures of minerals, later the minerals were mixed before smelting, and finally the separate metals were mixed to form the alloy. Bronze now means a copper-tin alloy but the objects labeled bronze in archeological collections range all the way from almost pure copper to nondescript mixtures in which lead, nickel, zinc and other metals are present as well as tin.

It may be well to stop here to explain why we now use so much more iron than we do other metals, almost a hundred times as much as any other one. One reason is that it can be made so cheaply, about one fifth the cost of any other metal, but the main reason is that it has so many good qualities. It can be cast, hammered, rolled, and drawn into wire, and separate pieces are easily joined by welding. More important is it that its hardness can be made anything we desire, a horseshoe nail is soft enough to bend in your fingers, while a razor blade is as hard as glass. Finally, it is unique in that having made it hard you can make it soft again and then reharden it. No other metal has this property to any important degree. While soft it is easily formed into any desired shape and it can then be made so hard as to keep a cutting edge, for example. It is most used because it is most useful.

The metallurgists in Roman times found they could turn copper into brass by burying it in powdered zinc mineral and heating it. They did not know there was any such metal as zinc, all they knew was that by treating copper in that way its red color changed to gold, they could make sound castings from it (they could not from copper) and it was easier to work this metal into desired shapes. It was not until 1780 that brass was made by fusing metallic zinc with copper.

Lead does not occur as a metal, but it is easily produced from its ores. Best of all, if there is any silver in the ore it goes into the lead, which can be separated from it by a simple process known as cupelling, and which yields a lead oxide that can be used as a paint pigment, in making glass, and in glazing pottery. Lead was easily formed into pipes and sheets, and the hanging gardens of Babylon had lead pans, for the same reason as a modern fern box has a metallic container of zinc or tin-coated iron. The Romans used lead pipe extensively for water-supply and plumbing and their lead mines in Spain were the largest and most extensive mining operations of the world up to that time. Mixed with tin lead yielded an easily fusible solder with which pieces of various metals could be securely joined. From it a white pigment could be made that for centuries was the basis of nearly all paint. When guns were invented lead was employed to supply the bullets and shot.

Lead was the first metal to play an important part in the development of modern learning. When printing from movable type was invented in Europe in the Fifteenth century lead alloyed with tin and antimony was found to be the most satisfactory metal for casting the type, for it makes a sharp impression and is easily recast when broken. (A modern newspaper recasts its type-metal several times in a day.) There are many other useful alloys of lead, and merely to name them would make a long list; one of them, pewter,[1] has recently come back into favor.

From the Fifteenth century to the beginning of our Century of Progress no important new uses were found for either copper or lead, only extensions of known uses. For example, the works of clocks began to be made of brass instead of wood. They perhaps even lost ground a little, for the in-

[1] Pewter contains more tin than lead.

troduction of tinware in the Eighteenth century not only made metal housewares available to the common people, but checked the growth of the use of copper, brass, and lead alloys for household purposes.

Our century was half over, indeed, before the growing knowledge of the nature and use of electricity began to create for all three of them a greatly increased usefulness. Copper felt its influence first because its conductivity for electricity is so much higher than that of any other metal except silver. Not only were miles of copper wire needed for the construction of the interior parts of generators and motors, but miles upon miles for the transmission lines between them and leading to the electric lights. One electric transformer recently built contained 15 tons of copper wire. Between 1801 and 1850 about $1\frac{1}{2}$ million tons of copper were produced in the whole world, two-thirds of it in Europe. North America produced only one-twentieth part of it, and it was all used for the purposes of the pre-electrical period.

In 1851 the United States produced a thousand tons of copper and in 1880 the output was 30,000 tons; half the increase took place between 1872 and 1880. By 1885 the yearly output was 82,000 tons and by 1890 it had reached 130,000. In 1900 it had grown to 303,000 and by 1910 the annual yield

of our mines was 540,000 tons of the red metal.
In 1926 it was 869,811 tons. During the six 10-
year periods ending with 1920 the average increase
in world production of copper per decade was 60
per cent, while in the United States it was almost
150 per cent. From contributing less than one
hundredth part of the world's copper in 1850 we
came to supply over half of it in 1890-1900; since
then our proportion has remained about the same.

Zinc also shared copper's new-found importance.
The rapidly growing electrical industry needed
large amounts of brass, not for any electrical qualities but because it is easily formed into intricate
shapes, has about the right hardness and a pleasing
color, and can be kept polished. Its effect was less
marked, because zinc as a separate metal had only
come into use in Europe a little before the beginning of the Nineteenth century and its use had
grown rapidly in the period following. It was
found that it produced an even whiter paint pigment than lead, could be rolled into sheets, formed
into articles, and was quite resistant to corrosion.
Best of all, it would protect iron sheets from corrosion if they were dipped in melted zinc. Even
today this last is its principal single use. Between
1841 and 1881 world production almost doubled
every decade.

Commercial production in the United States

began about 1860. Between 1871 and 1875 we produced 54,100 tons; between 1881-5 it rose to 180,127 tons; in 1891-5 to 411,975 tons; 1901-5 it reached 847,519 tons; and in 1911-5 attained 1,-814,576 tons for the 5-year period. Between 1914 and 1919 our output was temporarily greatly increased because Germany had captured that part of Belgium that was one of the principal zinc-producing regions of the world. We will return in a moment to the multiplying uses for zinc.

Lead first felt the impulse of electricity through that outgrowth of the telegraph, the submarine cable, for which it forms a flexible, waterproof outer sheath, through which marine creatures are disinclined to bore. A long time later came the terrestrial cable, when telephone and telegraph wires began to so congest the streets of our cities that it was evident that they must be placed in underground conduits. Such a cable employs about 3 pounds of lead for each pound of copper in it, so it is not remarkable that this is one of the principal uses of lead, consuming over a quarter of our domestic output.

The coming of the automobile made a new market for lead, used in old ways. Machinery of all kinds had long been using lead alloys as a low-friction bearing metal, though steel balls and rollers had come to contest for the privilege of serving in that way. It was used, too, in paint and solder. Eventually the self-starter not only provided the motorist with one of his greatest blessings, but also gave lead a new job, for the storage battery that actuates it is principally composed of that metal. Now this is the principal use for lead, requiring over 200,000 tons of the metal yearly.

Lead is curiously like a faithful workman who if he loses a job at one place can always get another. World production of lead had been about 24,000 tons yearly in the first decade of the 19th century, increased to 33,000 in the second, rose to 90,000 in the third, and 112,000 in the fourth. Between 1861 and 1870 it averaged 266,000 tons yearly and in the next decade rose to 372,000. Between 1891 and 1900 the yearly average was 784,000 tons and between 1911 and 1920 it was 1,203,000 tons. One great factor in the pre-electrical period of growth was the use of lead pipe for plumbing. Not only was it easy to make water-tight joints with lead pipe but it was easy to bend the pipes in placing them in a house that was already constructed.

But after the middle of our Century of Progress lead began to be superseded by iron pipe in building construction. Pipe-making had been so perfected that tight joints could be made with screwed connections, and since the piping was put in while the dwelling was under construction bends could be avoided. The increasing pressures in water-supply systems required a very heavy lead pipe to withstand them. Eventually brass pipes and copper tubing began to compete with iron pipe in performing that service. About the only place where much lead is employed in the plumbing of a modern house is to connect the toilet with the cast-iron waste-pipe. Lead not only lost that opportunity to serve, but as old houses were torn down the lead pipe was saved and sold in competition with new lead. It was fortunate for the lead producers that so many new uses were found for their product.

To list all the modern uses of lead would be as dull as Homer's catalogue of the ships. Such obvious uses as the "tin" foil wrappings in which cigarettes and pipe tobacco are packed, the sinkers on fishing-lines and nets, and the lead frames of art windows, need not be recalled, but some important uses are comparatively unknown to those who benefit by them. Many people know that lead is used in glass-making to produce a more brilliant product; imitation gems are made of it. But that kind of glass is also tough and capable of withstanding wide temperature changes without cracking. Consequently the glass tubes of Neon signs that make our streets so brilliant, radio tubes that bring us the news and entertainment of the whole

world, and the stems of ordinary lamp bulbs that
turn night into day for us, are made of glass that
contains as much as 22 per cent lead. Few of the
inhabitants of the tall buildings of our cities
realize that these structures rest on anti-vibration
mats made up of lead and asbestos sheets. The
new Waldorf-Astoria, in New York, employed 80
tons of lead for this purpose. Possibly the plant
that printed this book used similar mats under its
presses, for they are quite frequently used under
heavy machinery.

Most people know that the "ethyl gas" they buy
at the filling station derives its name from the lead
tetra-ethyl that has been added to the gasoline to
prevent the pre-ignition that causes "knock." If
their trip to the country results in an eruption
caused by poison ivy they probably know that the
best treatment is to apply a milky solution of
"sugar of lead." But another lead chemical is
widely used in refining the gasoline and there are
some three score or more of lead compounds that
are sufficiently useful in modern life to deserve mention. The one used in largest quantity, of those
not already mentioned, is lead arsenate, one of the
most potent weapons in man's unceasing warfare
against the insects that would destroy the plants
that he cultivates for food, clothing, and beauty.
The most important lead compounds, of course,

are the oxides and basic carbonates and sulphates that are used in paint and rubber. Since zinc compounds are used in the same way we had best talk about both at once.

Except for cheap red or black paint nearly all paint is originally white, the color being imparted to it by some suitable coloring matter, which may be either a solid pigment or a liquid dye. The essential constituents of a paint are some oily or gummy substance and metallic oxides. If an oil is used it must be the kind that turns into a gum by "drying" (really oxidation); gums are dissolved in a volatile solvent that evaporates. A number of different white pigments can be used, but for many centuries basic lead carbonate was, all around, most satisfactory. Then zinc oxide was introduced in competition with it, and it is generally agreed that a mixture of the two is better, for general purposes, than either alone. For special purposes each has its advantages; enamel paints, for example, use only zinc oxide, and for certain kinds of interior work a mixture of zinc sulphide and barium sulphate, known as lithopone, is used. Much more could be said about pigment, but this will have to suffice. How the subject ramifies is illustrated by the mention of lithopone, which naturally leads us to mention that it is extensively used for making painted cloth known as oil-cloth, because it is less likely to crack with age.   Added to ground cork it makes linoleum, and is also used in colored printing inks.

Perhaps few people realize that the rubber tires on their automobiles contain more mineral than they do rubber.   Possibly they are aware that the black color is imparted by carbon black, made from natural gas, but they probably do not know that some, or all, of the pigment substances referred to above are added to the rubber in such large amounts that it might well be said that the rubber was added to the pigments.   The reason for doing it is that the mixture gives better service than rubber alone, just as a mixture of cement with sand and stone is more serviceable than cement alone, and for the same reason, the physical structure is better for the service demanded of it.   Rubber is about as important as paint as a use for these substances, yet few people would ever think of themselves as riding on zinc-shod wheels.   Modern life is so complex that the imagination seems to have broken down under the strain of too many opportunities for its exercise.

Zinc also has many unobtrusive uses.   It has been popular of late to dramatize the uses of minerals by making a tale of them.   Thus we might say that a sleeper is wakened in the morning by an alarm clock, of which the works are brass and the

outer case nickel-plated zinc.   He cleans his teeth
with paste squeezed from a zinc tube, puts on shoes
of which the eyelets and tips of the laces are made
of zinc, and as he goes down to breakfast his eye
falls on numerous electrical fittings of brass, and on
walls and woodwork painted with zinc pigments.
Thus we might follow him through his days and
years, until finally after a service with music from
an organ of zinc pipes he is laid away in a cemetery
is a casket which may be of zinc, or copper, or of
lead.   The weakness of the method is that all
minerals enter so extensively into our modern life
and are used in so many combinations that an
equally impressive tale could be made for almost
any mineral substance,—fluorspar, for example.

Among the zinc compounds not already mentioned two are of outstanding importance.   Zinc
chloride is used to treat wood to keep it from decay
and a large quantity is used for the purpose yearly.
It is also used in soldering, in mercerizing cotton
and the oxy-chloride is used in tooth fillings and
in making artificial teeth.   The sulphate has a
great variety of uses, in dyeing and calico printing,
making glue, as a disinfectant, and for many other
purposes.   Scores of zinc compounds could be
cited, such as the zinc stearate powder used on
babies.   There are many other unobtrusive uses of
metallic zinc, such as the screw-caps on glass pre-

serve jars and collapsible tubes, the case of dry electric cells, in which it serves as one of the poles, zinc sheets for engraving, and so on. There are literally thousands of the operations of daily living that are most satisfactorily performed because zinc or one of its alloys or compounds is available.

Often these sons of Vulcan compete for the opportunity to serve man. This is true of all mineral substances, and one instance will have to serve to illustrate that general situation. The field in which there is widest and keenest competition is in providing a roof over his head. A half-dozen other minerals, as well as the three sons, all vie to serve.

Doubtless man's earliest protection from the weather was the stone of a cave, while a skin tent provided a portable shelter. In countries where wood was abundant shingles were more permanent than a straw thatch, when houses were built, but both were inflammable. Shingle roofs are now prohibited in many towns. Specially shaped brick, called tiles, are not only fire-proof but keep out the heat better in hot countries. Thin sheets of slate are somewhat lighter than tiles, but both are heavy and occasionally drop off on the heads of passers-by.

Metal roofs appeal because they can be made leak-proof and are more permanent. The Pantheon was roofed with lead and many monumental buildings built in and after the 15th Century have lead roofs, Lincoln cathedral in England is a beautiful one.   Many more buildings were built with copper roofs, and still continue to be.   Nearly all the buildings at Columbia University have copper roofs, while a recent description of a private home in California mentions that it employed 4000 pounds of copper for its roof, in addition to 1200 pounds of copper radiators and 1000 pounds of brass pipe.   After the beginning of the Nineteenth century sheet zinc began to be used for roofing. Each of these materials has some advantage, and usually also some drawback; producers see the advantages, while competitors are most keenly aware of drawbacks.

Roofs of more than one metal are common also. Tin-coated iron was once popular, but needs protection by paint, and its appearance is not liked. A cheaper substitute is terne plate, coated with a mixture of lead and tin.   Zinc-coated, or so-called galvanized, iron is excellent for industrial buildings where its appearance is not a factor.   This material, it might be remarked in passing, came near giving a demonstration of the workings of Gresham's law.   In the war period when prices were high some dealers began using such thin zinc coatings, to lower the price of manufacture, that it would not resist corrosion. The cheaper material began to monopolize the market and gave such unsatisfactory service that the whole industry began to be threatened; a serious matter, since this is the principal single use of zinc. Recently the Zinc Institute has copyrighted a "Seal of Quality" which it allows to be placed on material which bears a sufficient quantity of zinc. It is hoped that this will operate to restore the prestige of good quality zinc-coated roofing and enable its makers to sell in competition with inferior lower-priced products.

Flat, or nearly flat, roofs have to be absolutely water-tight, and asphalt or "tar," as it is commonly called, is quite satisfactory for this purpose, as it expands and contracts without opening cracks. Its surface is usually coated with gravel, so it can be walked on. Paper impregnated with asphalt can be used on sloping roofs and within the last couple of decades "composition shingles" of paper impregnated with asphalt and surfaced with crushed stone or slate have been used. Asbestos shingles are really tile, made from asbestos fiber and cement instead of clay. The way in which many of these mineral substances are put up is in large part due to the insistence of architects that a shingle roof has the most pleasing appearance, and no matter what the roof is made from it must have the general appearance of shingles.

This interlude has perhaps served to explain why although copper is a good roofing material, many other mineral substances are also used to serve the purpose of protecting dwellings from the weather. Many other uses for copper might be listed, and odd bits of data, such as that the Waldorf-Astoria has 569,000 pounds of brass pipe, 80,000 pounds of copper in radiators, 14,000 pounds of copper ware, and has two copper domes coated with aluminum foil, while a not very prominent maker of cosmetics uses 25,000 pounds of copper yearly in making rouge boxes and compacts, could be rehearsed. An electric-power transmission line in California has 50 strands in its cables, each 172 miles long, or 8600 miles of wire, weighing 2090 tons. Probably there are 100,000,000 miles of copper wire in use in the United States, four-fifths of it in telephone lines. This does not include the wire used in the construction of generators, transformers, and motors, which would add about 25,000,000 more miles. But enough has been said to indicate that copper, lead, and zinc still serve many old purposes and have found so many new ones that we have brought into use larger quantities in the past thirty years than were required in all man's history before that. A statistical study made two years ago indicated that in the preceding 41 years the average annual increase in the consumption of zinc in the United States was 6.14 per cent, of copper 5.78 per cent, and of lead 4.09 per cent. One does not need to be a mathematician to realize from this that not many years elapse before the increase in a year is a quantity greater than the total consumption of not long before.

One of the principal factors in creating these new uses has been the development of transportation. We have spoken of the early influence of the railroads. A recent[2] advertisement of the *Detroit News* proudly announces that "the automobile industry will lead the nation back to prosperity" by consuming 85 per cent of all the gasoline produced, 30 per cent of all nickel, 26 per cent of all lead, 17 per cent of all aluminum, 16 per cent of all iron and steel, 14 per cent of all copper, and 11 per cent of all tin, as well as rubber, lumber and cloth. Add to this the telephone, the radio, the motion picture, electric power plants, transmission systems, and lighting and important reasons for the tremendous growth that has taken place in consumption are easy to visualize.

Some thoughtful students of the commercial and technical problems of the metallic mineral industries are inclined to believe, however, that it is the building industry rather than the automotive that

[2] January 21, 1932.

offers the greatest possibility for increase in metal consumption. The automotive industry can prosper through supplying new cars for old, but since most of the material in old cars eventually comes back on the market as reclaimed metal, unless the number of cars per capita continues to increase it is possible to imagine a future situation in which the metal reclaimed from scrapped automotive vehicles could supply that required to build new ones.

In the construction of buildings, especially private dwellings, wood and non-metallic minerals have been chiefly employed. Wood shrinks on drying but expands again if it becomes damp, and this makes trouble when it is employed in combination with minerals, such as plaster on lath. To apply plaster, lay bricks, or set tiles requires much expensive human effort, and a dwelling house is much more expensive, in proportion to materials and workmanship, than an automobile, because the methods now used in its construction do not lend themselves to mass production. Studies of how to provide better homes at less cost are chiefly directed toward cutting down the man-hours of labor necessary. One means suggested is to use paneled sheets of metal, that can be quickly and easily attached, for wall construction. This is not the place to discuss the many and complex technical

and practical problems involved in such a change,
but what has been said will indicate that the ending
of a century of progress does not presage a slowing
up of progress, for there are many fields of knowledge and skill still to exploit.

CHAPTER VI

YOUR HUMBLE SERVANTS

ONE of the age-old ways in which man has used minerals is in building things. He piled up stones to make a fireplace, and as an eventual result learned to produce metals. He piled up other stones to make a shelter, used mud to fill the chinks, and from noting the effect of fire on the mud not only learned how to make bricks, but eventually all sorts of ceramic wares. It has been rather fashionable lately to sneer at the amount of progress that has been made in some of these activities. It is true that we still make a brick building by placing one brick on another, just as the Babylonians did, but it is also true that, so far as we know, Harpo Marx does not play the harp any better than King David could. When once the most satisfactory way of doing a thing has been found, progress stops, for there isn't any more progress to make along that particular line. The marble that Phidias used in carving his statues was as good as any that can be found today, and modern artists cannot carve better statues from it.

All that can be recorded for some of the materials of construction in our Century of Progress is a great increase in their quantitative use. Perhaps there is no modern building that uses more stone than some ancient ones, but there are many more big buildings. It is quite appropriate that one of the largest houses our own Department of Commerce at Washington. Some details as to the minerals used in its construction will illustrate how modern building construction differs from the earlier.

It covers an area of nearly eight acres and its seven stories have altogether 36 acres of floor space. Its supporting framework of structural steel weighs 16,400 tons. The outer walls contain 1100 carloads of limestone from Indiana and 150 carloads of granite from Connecticut. In a medieval building the walls would have had to support the whole structure and would have required much more stone. The roof consists of six acres of tile held in place with two tons of copper nails. The windows contain six acres of glass and the plastered walls and ceilings have an area of 99 acres.

In the interior there are 900 tons of marble from Missouri, 900 tons from Vermont, 860 tons of Mankato stone from Minnesota, 300 tons of wall and floor tile from Ohio, 35 tons of floor tile from West Virginia, 27,000 tons of terra cotta from North

Carolina and West Virginia, nearly two million
face and gray bricks from Pennsylvania and 70
million common bricks from the District of Columbia.   The flooring is mostly of terazzo, marble chips
laid on concrete.   The concrete flooring would
make a 5-foot sidewalk 400 miles long.

Though we are here concerned with non-metallic
construction minerals it is interesting to note also
that about 400,000 pounds of bronze has been used
in the solid sliding doors that guard the 19 en-
trances, in ornamental gates, and in fixtures and
fittings.   For heating 420 tons of radiators were
required, 400 tons of sheet iron was used in constructing ventilating ducts, while 16 carloads of
iron pipe, 8 carloads of brass pipe, and 2 carloads of
fittings were used in its construction.   There are
some 50,000 electric outlets, served by 568 miles
of copper wire.   There are 1600 telephones and its
200 electric clocks are controlled by a master clock.
Since the steel framework expands and contracts
the building is constructed in three sections, with
a 2-inch separation provided with an "accordion
joint" of copper.   The whole structure is sup-
ported on 80 miles of concrete piling.

Modern buildings, therefore, use a greater
variety of mineral substances, not only because
they have new mineral things in them, such as
telephones, plumbing equipment, elevators, and

many others, but they also use a greater variety
of minerals in their construction. This is because
the improvement of transportation has made it
practicable to bring materials from a great distance to secure a desired effect. Most light-
colored stone buildings in the United States are
built of limestone from Indiana. The interior of
the Chamber of Commerce Building in Washington
is made of a similar stone brought from France
because that gives the best effect with the "hone
finish" the architect desired. Many people ad-
mire the glistening white interior of the Library of
Congress, made of marble brought from Italy. A
modern bank, or other elaborate building, will
sometimes use stone brought from a half-dozen
different places in order to give the desired color
effects. Many recent buildings in New York use
for their lower stories an irridescent dark stone,
technically known as laurvikite, brought from
Norway.

There has been much development in the use of
artificial stones. Modeling in clay and hardening
it by burning seems almost as old as man. Using
slacked lime, which hardens on exposure to the air,
is also thousands of years old. Much more recent
is the use of calcined gypsum, commonly known as
"plaster of paris." Originally used for applying
decorations in relief, like the frosting of a cake, its

uses have greatly multiplied. The Exposition at Chicago in 1893 was an impressive demonstration of the remarkable effects that can be obtained with it, at a minimum expense, in the construction of temporary buildings. It has long been used for the final finishing coat on most plastered walls, but lately it has begun to be extensively used in the construction of partitions within buildings, either in the form of large sheets composed of fibre and gypsum, or solid blocks. The five million tons that is used yearly in the United States supplies these uses and a host of others; for this, like most other mineral substances, has many other uses besides its most obvious ones. Glass makers use it by the ton in preparing the beds on which they polish plate glass, farmers apply it to the soil, and cement manufacturers use thousands of tons of it to retard setting. Ground gypsum, known as terra alba, is used in paper and paint. Rubber, phonograph records, buttons, and many other things contain gypsum. The chalk used in school-rooms is not chalk at all, but moulded gypsum. A quite recent development is acoustic plaster. Something that will develope gas, such as calcium carbide, is mixed with the plaster, giving it a spongy structure and a rough surface that does not reflect sound waves, and thus does not echo like a smooth and solid wall.

The outstanding development in the past century among construction materials is portland cement, which derives its name from the fact that someone thought that artificial stone made with it looked like the natural stone from Portland, England. Though the development was almost wholly within the century the idea was old, for the Egyptians used a mixture of lime and clay in building operations. Experiments made about 1750 led to the patenting, in 1824, of making a cement by burning the clay-lime mixture and then adding water to the ground product. Early work in the United States indicated that a pretty good cement could be made by burning natural rock of the right composition; all the cement made here before 1875 was of that kind, and nearly 2 million barrels of it are still made yearly. It was found, however, that a better product could be made by mixing lime and clay, and 172,000,000 barrels of that kind were made in the United States in 1929. But to be accurate, it should be added that an important fraction of the quantity just given was produced by mixing lime and blast furnace slag.

The making of portland cement is one of the most interesting and dramatic of modern manufacturing operations because it is carried on in a refractory-lined steel cylinder, large enough to drive an automobile through and as long as a 20-

story building is high. It is inclined three-quarters of an inch to a foot, and since gravity would naturally make it slide down as it turns over, its supports are so cleverly constructed that it tends to screw itself up just as much as it does to slide down, and thus stays in the one place. Powdered coal, fuel oil, or natural gas is used to produce heat, and the temperature at the finishing end is 2500°F. but gradually declines to 1000°F. at the point where the ground and mixed materials enter. The cylinder turns over in one or two minutes and the material gradually works its way to the hot end.

The burned material passes through a shorter cooling cylinder, where it gives up its heat to the air used for combustion of the fuel in the other. It is then ground so exceedingly fine that 78 per cent of it will pass through a screen having 40,000 apertures per square inch. Some six million of the average-sized particles in portland cement would be required to cover a square inch. The ground material is kept for a time, as it is believed it thus improves in quality. It is packed for shipment in barrels holding 376 pounds, or in cloth or paper sacks holding one cubic foot. This is done with automatic devices and the paper sacks have double walls and are tied with wire while still empty, after which they are filled through a valve in the bottom. Although 85 per cent of the sacked cement is in cloth the industry requires 100 million paper sacks yearly. The cloth sacks are supposed to be returned for refilling, but some 60 million of them fail to come back each year, and 34,000 miles of 30-inch wide cloth is needed to replace them.

The cement industry is one of the important consumers of fuel, using 10,000,000 tons of coal and 5,000,000 barrels of fuel oil yearly. The output by weight amounts to about 25,000,000 tons per year and it sells for a price that represents only an operating margin over the cost of what has been done to the original raw materials.

The uses of portland cement are so evident and so many that all that seems necessary is to refer to its general function in concrete, which is composed of some such general ratio as one part by volume of cement, three of sand, and five of crushed stone. Theoretically this is so the sand particles will fill the apertures between the stones, and the cement all the apertures that are left. The wetted cement hardens, adhering firmly to the stone and sand and cementing all to a solid mass. Only enough water to combine with the cement should be used, as the aim is to produce an aggregate in which there are no voids. It must be kept moist until it has set, otherwise it will lose water by evaporation. A new variety, already of great importance, attains its set very quickly.

One of the important modern uses of concrete is for highway construction, something like 50 million barrels being used for that purpose yearly. The design of these roads is interesting. Since the concrete expands slightly with heat a mile of solid concrete would be 3 feet shorter in winter than in summer. Provision for this must be made, and it is afforded by casting the road in 20- to 50-foot sections, placing asphalt-impregnated paper between them. The asphalt stretches without cracking in the winter and a slight give in each of the numerous joints per mile takes care of the change of length. Another problem is support of the surface. Strength is imparted to the slab by embedding steel reinforcing, either rods or heavy wire mesh, in it. Support beneath is provided by smoothing and rolling the base and if settlement occurs later additional support can be provided by drilling a hole in the slab and forcing in thick mud under heavy pressure. When the slab is first cast it is immediately given a top coat of thin asphalt which not only prevents evaporation of the water of the mixture but prevents water from seeping in and causing destruction by freezing in winter. Such a road is expensive to construct, but is economical because of its long life and the low cost of maintenance.

Another important use of concrete is for fire protection of the steel work of modern buildings. The steel work is designed to support the building with safety at ordinary temperatures, but when the steel is heated to 1000°F. it loses half its strength. Since a fire in an hour will reach a temperature of 1700°F. a "fireproof" building needs to be resistant to damage by collapse rather than to destruction by fire. Columns and beams are therefore buried in concrete, the thickness used being designed on the basis of careful tests as to how long a fire can rage in contact with such a beam without causing cracking of the concrete or appreciable heating of the steel within. One and one-half to two inches of concrete will protect the steel for about four hours, giving opportunity to extinguish the fire. The cement also protects the steel from atmospheric corrosion, so it serves a double purpose.

Mention has already been made of the use of gypsum to produce a non-echoing wall surface. Everyone is familiar with the artificial stone blocks, composed chiefly of cement and sand, that are often used in the foundations for dwellings, but few realize the extent to which artificial stone now enters into building construction and decoration. Perhaps the most noticeable place is in the show-windows of stores, but the imitation of the appearance of natural stone is so faithful that in many cases only an expert can tell whether or not it is artificial.   No figures are available as to quantity or value of this material produced annually, but those most familiar with it agree it is surprisingly high and constantly increasing.

A modern problem in building construction is heat insulation.   Studies reveal that much of the heat generated within a building immediately escapes and the quantity thus lost is so great as to make it worth while to go to some expense to prevent it.   As usual, a number of mineral substances compete for this service.   One interesting one is slag wool, produced by the effect of a jet of air on melted slag of the proper composition.   This can be blown into the spaces between walls, made up into felt-like sheets and applied, or used in various other ways.   It stops the circulation of the air that leads to heat loss by convection.

Another substance that acts in the same way is diatomaceous earth, a deposit formed from an accumulation of the siliceous skeletons of diatoms. Years ago it was principally used in the manufacture of dynamite, but very little of it is now used for that purpose.   It can be placed loose in walls, is made up into bricks, and slabs, and has a variety of other uses, such as a filtering medium, almost as extensively as an abrasive, and it has been found to be useful in concrete.   Over a million dollars worth is produced yearly.   There are so many mineral abrasives, and they serve so many and such different purposes, that to attempt to discuss them would require too much space. The temptation to do so is strong, for much of interest attaches to them. We produce a half-million dollars worth of garnet yearly, for example, not as a precious stone but for use in wood finishing. The huge grindstones formerly used to produce wood pulp for paper-making are beginning to be displaced by built-up wheels to which artificial abrasives are attached. The use of artificial abrasives is steadily growing.

Heat resistance is even more important than heat insulation in modern industry. A familiar example is the spark-plug of an automobile, the main mass of which must be a non-conductor of electricity, and consequently non-metallic, yet able to resist the high heat and repeated shocks of the explosions in the cylinder. Ordinary porcelain was at first used, but laboratory study revealed that a different composition gave better results. This resulted in a search for commercial supplies of the minerals that produced the required structure and composition. Sillimanite, kyanite, and andalusite, minerals that had previously been only the objects of scientific study, now were sought and produced commercially. It was, as usual, found that the new material had many uses besides those for which it was produced, and it now displaces porcelain in many services in which heat resistance is essential.

The furnaces in which metallurgical and chemical operations have to be carried on must be able to resist high temperatures. In some steel furnaces the side walls are made only one brick thick, laid without any cementing material, so that the air leaking in around them will keep them from melting down, so difficult is it to obtain material to resist the high heat. The chief problem arises when the material being treated is basic in composition, and thus requires basic hearth and wall material to resist fusion. Lime produced by burning limestone would be cheap and effective as far as resisting the heat is concerned, but as soon as moist air touches it a compound is formed that is decomposed by heat, so it is impracticable to use it. A natural material that is a mixture of lime and magnesia is much better than lime and is used extensively for repairing the furnaces. Then magnesia, produced by calcining the natural mineral magnesite, was employed and found to be highly satisfactory, as it has a melting point of 5072°F. It can be manufactured into brick, and an extensive business in its production and use has developed. It is an essential in the steel industry, for example, which uses furnaces with walls made of magnesite bricks, and bottoms built up of granular material. The bricks were first made of burned magnesite, but laboratory studies revealed that they could not only be more cheaply made of the raw magnesite, but gave better results, and so could be used for some services where the others could not; for example, the kilns described as being used in making portland cement. At one time we imported much of our necessary supply of magnesite, but now we produce over a million dollars worth of the crude material yearly, chiefly in Washington and California. The value of the finished products is, of course, much greater.

Talc to most people at once suggests face-powder, but that is a rather unimportant use of it, from the standpoint of quantity used. Ground talc is used as a filler for paper and in rubber, paint, and textiles, in glass making, as a polish for peanuts and rice, to prevent rubber from sticking to the rollers used in manufacturing it, and to coat the surface of "composition" roofing so it will not stick when rolled. Crayons and pencils are made from it for use on slates and metals. Large slabs of it are made into laundry tubs, sinks, and the tops of laboratory tables. Switch-board panels, and a variety of other things that must be non-conductors of electricity, yet can be bored and cut, are made from it. Aquariums, acid tanks, furnaces and store fronts are made of it, as are fireless cookers and griddles. It has been found that a little added to concrete makes it less water absorbent. We produce over $2,500,000 worth yearly and import over a half-million dollars worth, chiefly of the high quality used in toilet preparations.

The fluorspar produced in the United States is worth as much as the talc, but few people outside the mineral industry would ever hear of it except by listening to tariff debates. That is because it is mostly used in making something else or in combinations. It is a practical essential in steel-making, where it is added to the slag of the open-hearth, making it more fluid. We use it also in glass, where it produces opalescence or an opaque white material resembling marble. It is an essential constituent of the white enamel on bathtubs and bath-room fixtures. Some of it is added to the mixture in portland cement-burning. The hydrofluoric acid that can be made from it will etch glass, but patterns on glass are usually made by directing a jet of sand or other abrasive against it. A small quantity of fluorspar is used for optical purposes, where it is useful in correcting color and spherical aberration errors in lenses. Thus we come into contact with it frequently in our daily lives, even though we fail to notice it.

Asbestos is more widely known, since its fire-resistant qualities and fibrous texture have attracted attention throughout the ages. It is really three kinds of minerals, according to the precise scientists, that are all capable of being worked into flexible fibres that can be spun into yarn and woven into cloth. Its most visible application in this form is for fire-protection curtains in theatres, but a much more important way in which it daily safeguards our lives is in the brake-bands and clutch-facings of automobiles, both as to importance of service and quantity employed. A thin sheet of it is employed between the head and the rest of the motor engine, and in many other types of machinery. These sheets of asbestos paper are also used as heat-insulating pipe-covering, sheeting between floors, and in lining safes, filing cabinets, and stoves. It provides the necessary packing to prevent leakage of steam where the piston rod comes out of a steam cylinder. Its use in making roofing tiles has already been mentioned, and it is also used in fire-proof cements and paints, and in a long list of other ways. The varieties of this mineral that we have in this country are not so well suited to its industrial uses as those obtained from foreign lands, so we import a large part of what we need, mostly from Canada, though South Africa has also recently become an important source of supply. Our people are so skilled in its preparation for use that the value of the manufactured products made from it that we export yearly is nearly half the ten million dollars worth of raw material that we ordinarily import; and even that figure does not include the asbestos used in finished products, such as automobiles, that we also export. It will be evident that nearly all the uses of this mineral lie within our century of progress in employing minerals in the service of man.

Barite, unlike asbestos, is almost unknown to the general public. Here again the reason is because it is used in combinations. Two-thirds of it is used in making lithopone, a mixture of barium sulphate and zinc sulphide that was mentioned in the previous chapter as one of our most important white paint pigments; one that has not only important uses of its own, but has other uses than as a pigment. The ground natural material is also used as a filler in making linoleum, oil-cloth, rubber, paper, and paint, and a quarter of our yearly supply is used in this way. The remainder is used in making barium chemicals, of which the most important is the sulphate, which has the same composition as the natural material, only refined. Any one who is about to be X-rayed has to drink quantities of a buttermilk-like mixture composed of barium sulphate stirred up with milk, since it coats the walls of the stomach and intestines and makes them visible under the impact of the rays. We use half of the world's output and import some of our supply from Germany, the other most important producing country. About two million dollars worth of the raw material is produced here each year, but the manufactured products made from it are worth more than ten times that sum.

When graphite is mentioned most people feel a gentle glow of satisfaction in the consciousness of knowing that lead-pencils are made of that instead of real lead. Possibly they will recall, too, that it got its name from the Greek word meaning "to write." Perhaps they would be surprised to learn that the material in a pencil is usually less than half graphite, and that three other uses far outrank it. By far its most important use is in the foundries where metal castings are made from molten metal. The mold for the casting is made by carefully burying a pattern in sand, so treated that it will keep its shape after the pattern is removed. The surface of the mold is then either dusted or "slicked over" with graphite so as to give it a smooth surface and keep the metal from sticking to it, much as a cook greases a baking-pan. Talc is also used for the purpose and probably more of it is used in this way than for dusting noses. Graphite is preferred and mostly so used, thousands of tons of it yearly.

Graphite paint is the next most important use and over 5000 tons of the mineral is used for that purpose. The reader will probably at once think of stove polish, but that only requires a tenth as much. Some other mineral pigment must be used with graphite in paint, as it does not work well alone; for example, it would give a satin-like surface to which a second coat would not stick. In proper mixture it gives remarkable resistance to acid fumes, heat and corrosion. Because it has thus to be mixed the natural crude mineral is finely ground without purification and sells for three or four cents a pound after grinding.

For melting brass and the high-grade variety of steel known as crucible steel crucibles of the general shape of a beer-keg, though of all sizes, the largest holding half a ton, are required. They are about half graphite and the rest clay and sand. Some five thousand tons of the mineral yearly is used for this, as compared to about 2000 employed in pencils. Two thousand tons are used in making the brushes that furnish the electrical contact with the commutators of motors and electric generators, because it wears evenly and decreases sparking. Stove polish has been mentioned but the quantity used as a lubricant is even larger. Sometimes it is mixed with oil or grease and sometimes is used alone, as in pianos and organs, where oil or grease would be objectionable on wooden parts that have to move. The grease put on the threads of pipes when they are screwed together contains graphite. Every boy has used it on his bicycle chain. Graphite imparts the shine to gunpowder (though that is not the reason for using it), and is used to polish shot. It is even used on tea leaves and coffee beans. Nearly a hundred tons is used each year in making electrotypes, where it is used both on the molds for the wax forms and on the surface of the forms before electroplating them. It has many other small but important uses, as in the packings mentioned under asbestos. Except for its use in pencils, nearly all its services to man have developed within, or not long before, our century of progress.

Mica is a familiar mineral, because everyone has seen flakes of it sparkling on the bottom of brooks or on the Christmas tree, and those brought up in the country associate it with the grateful warmth of the family stove, though they probably called it isinglass. This is another mineral whose greatest importance derives from its use in electrical industry. It easily splits into thin leaves that have a high resistance to the passage of electric current. Probably everyone has noticed the mica washers on the electrical connections of the toaster on his breakfast table, as well as the sheet of it on which the heating wires are wound. Its uses in electrical equipment are simply legion, but the most important is as the insulation between the segments of the commutator of generators and dynamos. For this use it must be carefully selected, because the natural mineral is likely to have small particles of other minerals, that are electric conductors, embedded in it. Besides its resistance this use depends on its not wearing down any faster or slower than the copper segments it separates, and thus maintains a smooth surface. As a result of the demand for super-quality the value of that we import is about five times our product, although it is only about one-third as much in quantity. Pieces of large size are much more valuable than smaller ones, though for many uses large sheets can be built up with the aid of a cementing material that is also of a high electrical resistance.

The largest amount of mica is used in making composition shingles and roll roofing, where it is applied to the inside surface to keep them from sticking together when piled in packs or rolled up. It is used in the making of rubber tires, as a lubricant inside the shoe, in lubricants, and it imparts the shine to wall-paper. It is not, however, the substance that glistens in concrete station platforms and stair-treads; that is carborundum, which has been added to give the surface ability to resist the wear of scuffling shoes with a little sand on their soles.

Salt is a mineral that man seems always to have used, for he needs it in his food, perhaps because his remote ancestors lived in the sea. That that is not now its principal use may be inferred from our using in the United States some 16 times as much salt per person as the Chinese do. Since it is taxed there they use it more sparingly in food than we do, but we mainly use it for other purposes. Salt is one of the principal raw materials of chemical manufacture. From it we make sodium carbonate and sulphate and hydrochloric acid, and these are in turn used to make many other things. Sodium carbonate, for example, not only yields the familiar bi-carbonate, caustic soda, and a tremendously long list of other compounds, but has many important uses of its own. It and sand are the principal constituents in glass. That, of course, is a very old use but many of the chemical substances of which sodium is a base are quite new, for example, the sodium cyanide that is used to dissolve gold out of its ores. Thus again we see that our increasing need of this old mineral

derives from having found new uses for it, as well
as new uses for old products, such as the glass in
electric light bulbs.   Cheap as salt is, we use over
$25,000,000 worth yearly; or over 8 million tons.

Feldspar is an unfamiliar servant because it
does not appear in person. Yet we have it in
daily use, for it forms from one-tenth to one-third
of the material from which porcelain, pottery,
white ware, vitrified sanitary ware (as distin-
guished from enameled iron) and enameled brick
are made.   Glazes on earthenware are one-third
to one-half feldspar.   The enamel on bath-tubs and
other bath-room equipment is largely composed of
feldspar.   It is also added to glass, especially
opalescent and white glass.   Artificial teeth are
made of it.   It is also added to scouring soaps for
use on material that sand would scratch, while
important uses that absorb considerable quantities of the lower-grade material produced in mining
operations is for the facing of cement blocks made
to resemble granite, as a surface coating on composition shingles, and for stucco and pebble-dash
work in building construction.   The crude material produced yearly (200,000 tons) sells for less
than $2,000,000 but the products made from it are
many times more valuable.

Borax is an old friend, having long been used in
soap and for adding to the water used in washing.

Its main present use is in the enamel used on bath tubs and bathroom equipment, but it is also used in pottery, glass-making, in soap and glue, and for giving paper a glaze. Large quantities are used in cloth manufacture and in tanning leather. We used to import some of our supply but so much of it is now produced as a by-product of potash-making in California that we export over 50,000 tons yearly. The producers are systematically stimulating its use and are finding that some present users can profitably employ it more freely, it can be added to mixtures to advantage, and some who have not used it can benefit by it. The modern spirit in industry is to try to find beneficial uses for its product, not simply to push it in competition with something else.

Fuller's Earth is an old mineral that has lost its original employment and now is used only for a modern purpose. It is a special variety of clay that, because of peculiar physical structure, will remove the color and turbidity from oil, either vegetable or mineral. That was not its original use, however. Fullers were people who removed the grease and dirt from cloth, after weaving, by treating it with this kind of clay. One may think of it as a sort of soap, perhaps. Its use for that purpose is practically obsolete in America, though it still persists in Europe. Of the 300,000 tons, worth about $15 per ton, produced in this country almost all is used in clarifying oils, principally, of course, in petroleum refining plants. It can be used several times and then reconditioned, but finally has to be thrown away. It can be, and is employed for many of the minor uses of clay, and for such purposes may be considered clay. It is mentioned here as another example of a long-familiar mineral that is almost entirely used for a modern purpose.

Many more non-metallic minerals that serve modern man might be mentioned, but these must suffice. Enough has been said to indicate that, as with the metals, our greatly increased consumption has arisen from finding new uses for them rather than a more extravagant use for old purposes. On some we have economized, notably so in brick walls, where the steel frame has cut down the requirements to a small fraction; a modern tall building could not, of course, be built of brick alone. The progress of science has indicated how to mix minerals so as to get better results than with one alone. Several substances have been mentioned as being used in bath-tub enamel and to them might be added quartz, cryolite, lead, tin, and antimony oxides and, as coloring matters, many other mineral substances. The variety of mineral substances used in other branches of ceramic work is equally impressive. Impressive, too, is the great number of uses a single mineral substance has, and equally enlightening is the way in which different substances compete to give the best performance in a general class of uses. The latter is, indeed, one of the most striking features of our century of mineral progress, and while the humanist would perhaps sniff at it, it is an admirable striving after its own ideal of perfection.

CHAPTER VII

THE JUNIOR METALS

IF THE question be asked as to whether we mean junior in usefulness or junior in importance the reply is both, so far as the leading one, aluminum, is concerned. So recently as 1883 the production of aluminum in the United States did not exceed 83 pounds yearly though, according to Clarke's computation, aluminum is half again as abundant as iron in the earth's crust. Its compounds are indeed abundant, but up to that time nobody knew how to produce the metal from them at a cost that made it practicable to use it for anything except a chemical curiosity. There are two reasons for this.

One is that although aluminum is so much more abundant than iron in the earth's crust it does not have the fortunate habit of iron of occurring in large bodies of quite pure oxide. Iron ore containing 50 per cent iron is abundant and can be put directly into the furnace; aluminum ore is not very abundant, contains about 25 per cent aluminum, and has to go through an expensive purification process before reduction. The other reason is that aluminum can not be easily produced from its oxide. In the case of iron a ton of coal (in the form of coke from which valuable by-products have been recovered) is sufficient to produce a ton of iron, by taking the oxygen away from the iron oxide in a suitably constructed furnace. Unfortunately coal cannot take the oxygen away from aluminum oxide, just as a boy cannot take an apple away from a man, although he could easily take it away from a smaller boy. The first method was to use a big man, sodium metal, which could take the oxygen away from the aluminum. A 22-year-old student, Charles W. Hall, found in 1886 that if he dissolved aluminum oxide in a fused bath of cryolite, and then passed an electric current through it the metal could be produced. Unfortunately it takes about 25,000 kilowatt-hours of electric energy to produce a ton of aluminum and since $1\frac{2}{3}$ pounds of coal is required to generate a kilowatt-hour of electric energy in an average steam power plant, a little simple arithmetic shows us that the equivalent of 20 times as much coal (without any by-product recovery) is required to make a ton of aluminum as a ton of iron. Therefore aluminum is generally produced with electricity generated by water-power at places where there is no other market for the power and consequently it is cheap. With iron at about one cent a pound (in the form of pig iron) and aluminum at 23 cents per pound when in finished form ready for use it is clear that the difference between them in selling price must be mainly a difference in cost of production, remembering that iron is made on such a big scale that a single modern furnace will produce two million pounds of it in one day, or half as much as the production of aluminum in the whole country in a week.

When the price of aluminum was first reduced from dollars per pound to cents per pound many people jumped to the conclusion that it could at once be used in tremendous amounts for a great variety of purposes. Many of the older generation can remember some of the wildly optimistic articles that appeared forty years ago. They were entirely too optimistic, for much work remained to be done in bringing the metal into practical use. Some of the early claims were quite unfounded, such as that it would not corrode. It was at first difficult to produce the metal without its having small amounts of impurities in it, and these acted like little electrolytic cells, causing the metal in contact with them to corrode. Alkalies attack even the pure metal. An even greater practical difficulty is that pure aluminum is too soft to serve for many of the uses that were hoped for it, and most of the things that were added to it to harden it not only made it less resistant to corrosion but also made it difficult to work. In the case of most of the common metals the producers sell them in ingot form to fabricators, who work them up into articles that can be sold to consumers. The fabricators found so much difficulty in first working with aluminum that they tended to throw it up as a bad job, and the producers had to take over the task of producing not only the metal but consumer's products as well.

Finally, through the brilliant work of clever investigators, it was found possible to harden aluminum somewhat after the manner of hardening steel, though the process differs enough so it was not easily developed. Now the metal can be made as strong as steel, though only one-third its weight. The hardened material is not so corrosion resistant as the pure metal, and eventually a process was perfected to coat the hardened material with an outer layer of pure aluminum. Finally it was found practicable to make the metal in large pieces, and users can now buy channels and eye-beams as they can of steel.

The difficulty remains, however, that the price is necessarily much above that of steel, and consequently uses must be sought where the lightness is valuable enough to more than compensate for the added cost. Air-craft is an obvious application, and the growth of air transportation has hinged to a large degree on the development of these light alloys. Surface transportation has not been so responsive as was at first hoped. It was at one time thought that much aluminum would be used in automobile manufacture; for example, in casting the engine block and in fabricating the bodies. One fine car has an engine block of aluminum but the others have adhered to cast iron, while steel for body construction is almost universal. An important use, however, is in the pistons, which must be started and stopped many times a second and thus waste much power if they are heavy. Another important use is in building trucks, which if constructed of aluminum weigh no more when loaded than an ordinary empty truck does. Another possibility is in constructing Pullman cars, which have for an average paying load 12 passengers. They weigh about 10,000 pounds per passenger,[1] and much power could be saved, as well as less damage done to the roadbed at high speeds, if this weight could be reduced. Several railroads are testing this possibility, and also the practicability of constructing freight cars of aluminum; the outcome will be awaited with interest.

Meanwhile aluminum has found many impor-

[1] Contrast them with light automobiles, which weigh about 400 pounds per passenger.

tant uses.   Household utensils made of it are familiar to everyone, and their use was promoted by the
discovery that finely divided steel, known as steel
wool, has just the right hardness to polish kitchen
utensils easily and without scratching them.
Griddles made of aluminum can be used for cooking without greasing them, thus facilitating the
work of cooking.   When exposed to the air aluminum either remains bright or acquires a light-
colored matte surface that is attractive.   The pure
metal can be rolled into thin sheets and has won a
large place for itself in competition with tin and
lead foil as a wrapping material, especially for
candy and other food products.   The search of the
producers has been for uses that aluminum serves
better than any other material.   They are handi-
capped in this by the relatively high production
cost of the material.   It has, for example, a good
chance to compete with copper for electric current
transmission when copper sells, say, for 17 cents
per pound.   Although aluminum has only about
two-thirds the conductivity of copper it also has
only about one-third its specific gravity, so that a
pound of it makes a larger wire of the same length.
On this basis, for equal length and resistance,
aluminum is somewhat the cheaper metal and,
when various technical problems are taken into
account, competition is possible.   But finished

copper wire, in 1931, sold for as little as $8\frac{1}{2}$ cents per pound. Thus price as well as physical characteristics have to be considered in selecting the best material to serve a human purpose.

Tin is an ancient metal that has found many new uses. In the ancient world it was used chiefly for making bronze and other alloys, such as pewter, which were important to the life of the time. The world now uses somewhat more than 150,000 tons of it yearly, or a little more than half as much as of aluminum. The United States uses about half of the world's tin, but produces none itself; it is generally true, indeed, that the countries that use it do not produce much. It is a much-travelled metal; ore from Bolivia may go to England for smelting and the metal be brought to the United States for manufacture into a kerosene tin that is sent to China and, when emptied, converted to some other use.

Here in the United States approximately a half of the tin is made into tin plate, or terne plate, a form of roofing material that is coated with an alloy of lead and tin instead of pure tin. For preserving foods tin plate must be used, and its employment for this purpose is so familiar that comment seems unneeded. Tinware for household use has had to meet the competition of so many other materials that the present generation has forgotten what an important part it played in our early economic development. The Pattison brothers began its manufacture in Connecticut in 1740 and initiated a system of marketing direct to the consumer through peddlers that had a profound effect upon our early development. In 1810 two-thirds of the tinware output still came from that state and the itinerant vendors of Connecticut merchandise persisted until the middle of the century under review.

Solder absorbs a little less than a quarter of the tin we use. This is an ancient use that under modern conditions has greatly increased, such modern things as automobile radiators and radio sets find it essential. The bearing metals referred to in connection with lead account for 10 per cent, or more, of the total; tin foil and tin tubes require about an equal amount. Chemicals and other products absorb a surprising amount and many people may be surprised to know that much tin chloride is used in the silk industry. Tin oxide is used in making enamels and there are a whole host of minor uses of tin, such as in organ pipes, pipes for soda and beer fountains, and even in the rubber industry.

Tin is a rather high-priced metal, but until 1900 it averaged around 20 cents per pound. From then on the price steadily advanced and in the war emergency of 1918 reached $1.10 per pound in

New York. The average for 1919 was 65 cents per pound, it fell to 30 cents in 1921, and climbed back to 65 in 1926. Since then the price has been steadily declining and at the time of writing (April, 1932) is 18 cents per pound. For the past twenty years many people have been commenting on the small reserve of tin which the world seems to have, and the fact that many of the uses to which it is put are such that it cannot be reclaimed and used over again, but is destroyed in use. The cost of collection of such things as tinfoil and tin tubes makes re-use impracticable. While people were worrying over the possibility of finding substitutes for tin its high price was stimulating production to increase faster than consumption. Alarmed by the existence of stocks about three times those needed for normal functioning of the industry, the producers began to restrict production early in 1931 and have since made further decreases in the production rate, without, however, decreasing the stocks or being able to check the steady decline of prices.[2] The moral of this tale is that an over-stock of a mineral, with a consequent low price for it, can occur simultaneously with concern as to the probable future supply of it.

[2] In May, 1932, it was announced that all the tin mines would cease producing until August, 1932, and then operate at only 40 per cent of capacity.

Antimony is an old metal that the world has never come to require in any very large amounts, except in war time when the lead-antimony alloy used for the bullets of shrapnel may be used in enormous quantities. One reason for this is that we use antimony without producing it. Lead ores often have antimony associated with them and in the smelting process the antimony goes along with the lead, finally emerging with it in the form of an alloy known as "hard lead." When this is used for pumps and valves it contains about 12 per cent antimony. That which contains 6 per cent antimony is used for constructing tanks, as roofing sheets, and a variety of architectural purposes for which pure lead is too soft. Storage battery plates contain 7 per cent antimony and a little tin; bearing metals have a variable composition but are typically about 9 per cent antimony and 4 per cent tin. Linotype metal contains 12 per cent antimony and stereotype metal perhaps twice as much. Solders often contain a little antimony. Its compounds are used in making enamels, in red rubber, and in medicine, so that like all the other minerals it has a great many uses that are quite essential to our comfort and convenience but may not require any very large amounts. Altogether the world is able to get along with about 25,000 tons of it yearly, and most of it comes from China, where the deposits are so large and rich that other possible sources of supply find it difficult to compete.

Arsenic is another old metal, and finds its principal modern usefulness as one of our mainstays in our warfare on the insects that damage the crops we are trying to raise. Boll weevils and potato bugs are thus the principal consumers of arsenic; lead arsenate being used for the former and copper arsenite for the latter. Glass-making is another important use for it, and a little is used in lead shot, which contains about 1 per cent arsenic. Important quantities of arsenic are also used in sheep and cattle dip, as a wood preservative, in paints, and in preserving animal hides. It will be noticed that almost all these uses hinge on its poisonous quality. The famous "606" of Ehrlich recalls its use in medicine, but it has a number of other uses in therapy. It is practically never used in metallic form and there are no world statistics of production, but it must be approximately the same as of antimony. Consumption varies a good deal according to agricultural conditions.

Another old metal of which the world does not require very much is mercury, known in trade by its ancient name of quicksilver. It is the only metal in common use that is liquid at ordinary temperatures and has always attracted attention for that reason. The ancients used it in gilding and our predecessors in making mirrors, but those uses are no longer important. Another old use is as a collector of gold in placer mining and gold milling; the gold sinks beneath the mercury surface and the other material passes on. Fifty years ago this was one of the most important uses for it, and the world's production of mercury in 1881 was almost equal to the output in 1927. It is the only important mineral whose consumption has not greatly increased in the past fifty years. Its declining use in gold production has been accompanied by an increased use in the electrical industry and in the detonators for explosives. Mercury arc rectifiers are the principal use for it in modern electricity, though various forms of automatic switches for electric refrigerators, oil burners, and many other types of apparatus are important to us. The mercury vapor light has many important uses, though it has not proved so generally useful as was once hoped. Thermometers are, of course, familiar to everyone.

Mercury compounds have multitudinous uses. A curious one is in the paint that is applied to ship's bottoms to prevent barnacles growing on them. The caps that explode cartridges and dynamite contain mercury fulminate; nothing else has been found that serves as well for this purpose, though diligent search has been made. Calomel and corrosive sublimate are ancient standbys in the pharmacist's shop. Embalmers use the latter, and it is also useful in wood preservation and calico printing. Vermilion is an artificially made sulphide of mercury that the Chinese have used for thousands of years as a red pigment; it is still our best red though there are many others to compete with it, sometimes under false pretenses. Chrome red, basic lead chromate, red lead, sulphide of antimony, and rouge are all mineral reds that are valuable (perhaps the ladies find the latter the most essential), but the true vermilion has a color that the others can not exactly imitate.

After noting all the ways in which this liquid metal is useful to us, it must be admitted that even the sum of them is not very large. Not until 1927 did the total of world output amount to as much as 4000 tons yearly. During the past few years the output has been 5000 to 6000 tons. It is possible that our requirements may be greatly increased, for a recent invention is a new type of boiler in which mercury is used instead of water as the liquid to be evaporated. The experimental work with these has been so encouraging that a third unit has been built, each one requiring over a hundred tons of the metal for its initial filling. Since quicksilver, even at present low prices, costs nearly a dollar per pound it is necessary to guard against loss of its vapor, so it is needless to say there will be no whistle on the new boiler.

It may be well to recall here the various metals that chiefly function in connection with the steel industry, and in their uses apart from that could rank only as junior metals. Manganese, elsewhere referred to in more detail as used so extensively in making all steel and as an alloy in manganese steel, has also many uses as a compound, but none as a metal used alone. Nickel and chromium, on the other hand, while finding their principal use in alloy steel, are extensively used for plating and have some other uses in pure metallic form. Tungsten has been elsewhere discussed; it might claim to rank next to the power minerals as a multiplier of the useful effects of work. Vanadium and molybdenum have only junior uses apart from steel alloys. Cobalt is commonly associated with nickel, and cobalt alloy steels are also useful. That was almost its only use, aside from the employment of cobalt pigments in ceramics, until recently, when a metal that does not form a carbide was needed to use with tungsten carbide in making a newly-invented type of cutting tools. Even at that a little more than a thousand tons of the metal is enough to meet the world's yearly requirement.

Magnesium ranks as a junior metal because although the world uses something like a million tons or more of its compounds yearly, as indicated in Chapter VI, the metal itself is only used in small amount, something like 600 tons yearly in the United States. The main use of magnesium has long been in deoxidizing and de-sulphidizing other metals, in light alloys, and in making castings for aircraft construction. There it is used in propellors, fuel tanks, ribs, struts, wheels, etc. For this purpose it is alloyed with 6 to 8 per cent of aluminum. Oddly enough, it is not made from the thousands of tons of magnesite produced yearly, but is a by-product of salt manufacture.

Cadmium is a newcomer to the field of service but has already won a place, as the world's output of it in 1930 was almost 2000 tons. When it was found that it could be recovered as a by-product in zinc production by the electrolytic method there was at first no known use for it. Attempts to substitute it for tin in solder did not work out, but lately it has found its field in electroplating, especially as an intermediate layer between chromium plate and the underlying metal. For this it is valuable enough so that even at a price of around 65 cents per pound its use continues to grow. It is also used in making fusible alloys and in pigments.

Bismuth, on the contrary, has long been available without finding any extensive use. Recovered as a by-product in lead refining, much more than the hundred tons or so actually produced yearly could easily be made available. Its principal function is in yielding alloys of low melting point. It is easy to make bismuth alloys that melt in boiling water, and one use for them of which much is hoped is in bending thin-walled tubes. After the filled tube has been bent the alloy is removed by a steam jet and the results, it is claimed, are better than with present methods. Another promising use is for setting stamping dies that cannot be embedded in alloys of higher melting point because of the resultant temperature effect on hardness. This is a good instance of the value to industry of systematic careful study. Sometimes, though, the study developes a substitute. One use of bismuth used to be in the fusible plugs that operate to set off a sprinkler system when a fire occurs. First certain waxes were found to serve as well, and now glass ampoules filled with light oil are used for that purpose. Fusible alloys that children can use to cast their own toy soldiers require a surprising amount of metal, and are likely to employ bismuth in increasing amounts.

Zirconium, which from the alphabetic aspect appropriately concludes this chapter, seems to belong to the future rather than the present. Widely disseminated through igneous rocks in a rather common mineral, zircon, it had a limited use, in the oxide form, in making refractories. Only lately has the metal, with a purity of 98 per cent, been commercially available at a price of $12 per pound. It is claimed that it can be used to produce a superior product in steel-making, and if that is confirmed in practice it may come into much more extensive use. Much work is being done in laboratories on its compounds, and no one can foresee what the outcome may eventually be.

CHAPTER VIII

THE MIGHTY MIDGETS

THERE are various mineral substances of which we at present use but small amounts, yet their importance to our comfort and convenience is almost impossible to estimate. The ancient example of this is the small pinch of salt in our daily food, but an even more striking and equally visible modern one is the tungsten filament used in an electric light bulb. Our whole electric lighting system, with its many generating plants and its network of current transmitting systems, together with the great number of men who work daily to keep it functioning, all have for their purpose the production of the light emitted by the tiny wire under the influence of the electric current. So little of the metal is required for this mighty social service that it has been estimated that less than a hundred tons of it suffices to produce all the bulbs, including radio tubes, that are manufactured yearly. Metallic tungsten costs about $1.50 per pound but if its social value were computed from the additional electric energy required to produce the same amount of light yearly by the older method it would have to be reckoned in terms of hundreds of thousands of dollars per pound. Strangely enough, the tungsten wire that is socially so important derives a considerable part of its effectiveness from the one per cent of thoria that it contains, and which imparts to it an enhancement of its properties similar to the effects produced on steel by the alloying elements discussed in a preceding chapter.

While this is the most outstanding example of a mineral which serves a purpose so important that the quantity thus employed seems almost fantastically insignificant, there are many other instances of this general relation. We are not even restricted to our century of progress in our selection of them, for gold throughout the ages has also had a social importance far beyond that indicated by its quantity. At no time in the world's history has its yearly output exceeded a thousand tons, yet our whole system of international finance is based upon it as a standard. It furnishes a striking contrast to tungsten, which serves by doing something, because gold serves chiefly through merely existing. Another contrast is that, save for some minor exceptions, no important new use for gold has been discovered in centuries of human progress, while the use of tungsten cited only dates from the beginning of the last quarter of the century under review.

Radium is the mineral substance that my readers will probably first think of as an example of something that is important though its quantity is small. Less than half a pound of the element has so far been produced in this country, and probably less than a pound in the rest of the world. Its current price of something like $225,000,000 per pound is based upon the expense of its recovery from the substances (chiefly uranium minerals) in which it occurs in microscopic proportions. Fortunately its present uses require only very small amounts of it, and it must be employed with the greatest care. A few years ago it was supposed that the quantity of it in existence in the world was so small that it needed to be treasured carefully, but since then important new reserves have been discovered in the Belgian Congo and in northern Canada. Its use in the treatment of cancer is too well known to need repetition. Dr. Howard Kelly has recently said that if radium had no more value than simply serving as a palliative in the treatment of cancer "it would be well worth all our efforts."

A recent use for radium is as an improvement on X-rays for the photographic examination of the internal structure of metals, enabling a thickness of as much as 10 inches to be penetrated. Perhaps the service it has rendered to science, and especially the electrical industry, through the new conceptions of the nature of matter it has made possible, is quite as great as its service to suffering humanity.

Helium is another mineral substance that needs but little discussion, since so much has been written about it. First discovered in the spectrum of the sun in 1868, a generation passed before it was detected on the earth, and probably not more than 100 cubic feet of this light gas had been produced before 1917, at a cost of about $2000 per cubic foot. Because it is almost as light as hydrogen, but not inflammable, the possibility of its use in lighter-than-air dirigibles was quickly recognized and our Bureau of Mines began to produce it, with funds provided by the Navy, from natural gas in which it occurs in small amounts. By 1931 its cost of production had been brought down to under $6 per thousand cubic feet and the government operated plant can produce it at the rate of a million cubic feet monthly. At that price it can compete with hydrogen on a cost basis, without counting on the safety factor. When an airship is inflated with either helium or hydrogen air gradually diffuses in through the envelope. When the hydrogen content has thus been reduced to 85 per cent the airship must be deflated because of fire and explosion risk and loss of buoyancy, and no safe and economical process of repurifying the hydrogen has been found. Helium, on the other hand, retains its safety, only losing buoyancy, and it can be repurified at a small cost. It is therefore not necessary for us to ask "What price safety?," but unfortunately no country in the world besides the United States has yet discovered a commercially practical source of helium supply within its borders.

Neon is a well-known recent addition to the list of mighty midgets, for its warm red glowing signs now lighten almost every Main Street. Present in the atmosphere in microscopic proportions it long evaded detection, and until Claude perfected his process for its separation (which in turn resulted from finding a practical use for it), it cost about $25,000 to produce a quart of neon. Now it costs about $7.50 per quart, and that quantity is enough for $1000 worth of sign, which requires about $75 worth of electric energy per year to keep it glowing. The quantity of gas required for all the neon signs produced in a year would about half fill an ordinary bath-room. Argon, krypton and xenon are associates of neon that are used in a similar way, but it would lead us into too many technicalities to attempt to discuss them.

Fluorine has a use that is of much social importance since it is used in frosting the inside of

electric light bulbs.   Here again there is no means
of ascertaining a ratio between its importance in
human living, and the amounts thus employed.

Beryllium is an element that apparently would
be of much service to man if it could be produced
in considerable amounts at a reasonable price.
Only a few pounds per day are now being produced
at a small number of plants.   Much of its value
derives from its having a specific gravity of only
1.85, or about two-thirds that of aluminum.   This
unfortunately ensures that no mineral containing
it can have a large percentage of it by weight, and
the only practicable source, beryl, not only contains but five per cent of beryllium but is a rather
rare mineral as well.   Enthusiasts predict that it
will soon be produced for less than $10 per pound,
but others are more doubtful, since its present
price is about ten times that.   How much use can
be made of it naturally depends to a considerable
degree on its price.   Its alloys with iron, copper,
and nickel are of the most promise of service.

Selenium, on the other hand, is already of much
service.   Electronic tubes have been described as
having "made a $500,000,000 industry out of a
vacuum."   They control the speed and security of
express trains; operate traffic lights on distant
highways; count the traffic on the Detroit-Windsor
bridge, turning in reports to a distant office; re-

verse by the action of their own shadows the rolling of 10-ton steel ingots; start, stop, and level fast passenger elevators; and ring an alarm in the boiler room when smoke appears at the top of a smoke-stack. But selenium, copper oxide, all the alkali and alkali earth metals, thorium, cerium, and uranium all show a lowering of their electrical resistance proportional to the intensity of the light to which they are exposed; thus they can be used directly to create a variable resistance, instead of relying on electronic tubes, which are also operated by light beams. As they show differences in their sensitivity to light waves of different length they offer possibilities for future development. But while the photo-electric properties of selenium are important and of much promise, the quantity required for this purpose is small, and most of the 150 to 200 tons of selenium produced yearly in the United States is used either in glass-making, where it is useful in making a red glass that will not be too opaque to light, or in rubber-making for vulcaniz-ing the rubber.

Tellurium is a related element for which no im-portant uses have yet been found, and most of the thousand or two thousand pounds produced yearly is used in scientific and experimental work, such as in rubber compounding. Until recently it has been difficult to work with, one of its problems being that workers sometimes acquire "tellurium breath," which is said to bear about the same relation to halitosis that the latter does to a rose. Recently it has been electrodeposited, and many such difficulties may be overcome. A promising use of it is as a surface coating on such metals as magnesium to give corrosion resistance. Chemical engineers seem to regard selenium and tellurium as two mineral substances of great possibilities.

Platinum is a mineral substance that has an interesting history. When the Spaniards first found it in Colombia, about 1735, associated with placer gold, they named it platina, because of its silvery color. At first there was no use for it, but as chemical and industrial technique advanced, its resistance to chemical attack, high melting point, and hardness created several uses, though up to the end of the 19th Century the chemist was the one principally interested in it. It provided him not only with a variety of chemical utensils, but also served as the catalytic agent in the "contact mass" employed in the process used for making concentrated sulphuric acid; its cost was a little less than gold.

There were numerous other uses for it, as contact points in the electrical industry, as the lead-in wire in electric light bulbs, for the wires of thermocouples, and in dental work. Finally it became

fashionable as a material from which to make
jewelry, much to the dissatisfaction of the chemist,
for this use absorbed large quantities, raised its
price, and was largely independent of price con-
siderations. By 1920 the price had increased so
much that platinum cost seven or eight times as
much as gold, and about three-quarters of it was
being used in jewelry. The high price stimulated
producers to increase their output, and the consumers for other than jewelry purposes sought to
find something else that would serve their purposes.
Some were successful, and it is, for example, no
longer used in making electric light bulbs, while a
large electric manufacturing company is reported
to have ceased buying it, having changed its de-
signs and procedure to such a degree that the
platinum that comes back into the plant from
scrapping old equipment is enough to meet its
needs. The high price also led to the discovery
of some new sources, notably South Africa.

Two more things that could hardly have been
foreseen happened. The depression following
1929 greatly curtailed the buying of expensive
jewelry, and the International Nickel Company,
which produces platinum as a by-product,
changed its metallurgical procedure in such a way
as to yield a larger amount. As a result the average price of platinum in 1931 was less than one-half

the 1928 average, and hardly more than a quarter of the average for 1920. The official price of the refined metal is now about twice that of gold and quite likely will be stabilized around that level. In 1913 Russia was supplying over 90 per cent of the world's output of platinum, but in 1918 Colombia yielded 70 per cent of the total, which in quantity was only one-fifth the 1913 output. In 1929 Russia was again yielding half the total and in 1930 Canada's output was about $3\frac{1}{2}$ times what it had been only three years earlier. South Africa produced 600 ounces in 1925 and five years later was producing 75 times that quantity, or about a quarter of the world total.

Platinum always has associated with it several related metals, notably palladium, rhodium, and iridium. Most people have heard that iridium is used to make the hard tip on the point of a gold pen. Actually most of the iridium is used for alloying with platinum, especially for its uses in electrical equipment, as it makes the platinum harder. Gold alloyed with palladium becomes white. To discuss all the "white gold" alloys would require too much space because various elements can be alloyed with it to make it look like platinum, but problems arise as to the relative ease of working the alloy and in obtaining a solder that will match it in color. Probably the most important use of palladium is to produce "white gold" for dental use. The price is about the same as gold but, as it has only half the specific gravity, a cubic inch only costs half as much. Some "white golds" used for dental purposes perhaps contain no gold at all but are chiefly palladium.

The principal use of rhodium has been to produce wires made of 90 per cent platinum and 10 per cent rhodium. If such a wire is joined to a pure platinum wire so as to form a closed circuit and if one junction be heated, an electric current will flow through the circuit; and this current is proportional in strength to the difference of temperature between the hot and cold junctions. Since the melting point of these wires is very high such a thermocouple furnishes an accurate way of measuring high temperatures. This important use does not require much rhodium and since it seems clear that increased amounts of it are to be available in the near future additional uses are being sought. One is already available in that the platinum-rhodium alloy can be used as the contact mass in oxidizing ammonia to nitric acid. Other possibilities are rhodium-plated reflectors in automobile headlights and rhodium plating of solid silverware to protect it from tarnishing.

Osmium, one of this group, and the heaviest metal known, occurs naturally alloyed with iridium. It is this natural alloy which is used for the tips of gold pens. Ruthenium is the final member of the group; it has no outstanding uses.

Tantalum was discovered more than a century ago but for a hundred years it was impracticable to produce metal low enough in carbon content to be of any use. In 1903 it was made of sufficient purity to be drawn into wire and for a decade incandescent bulbs were made using it as the metallic filament. Then tungsten was found to be more satisfactory for the purpose. Recently it has been useful for thermionic tubes and a variety of chemical purposes, such as electrolytic devices and spinnerets in rayon making.

Cerium is a metal that everyone is familiar with, for the material that yields the spark in a pocket lighter is a cerium-iron alloy. The quantity required for this purpose is not large and its principal use is practically unknown to the public. Mixed with titanium oxide in the ratio of five parts of titanium to one of cerium, its oxide imparts a canary-yellow color to glass. There are a number of elements that belong to the same general group as cerium for which no important use has yet been found.

Caesium at first had no use, but when radio sets were operated from batteries it was desirable to keep the current consumption small, and caesium tubes, which produced an equal effect with much less current were proposed. It was found practicable to use them, but unfortunately it was also found practicable to connect radios with an ordinary lighting circuit, so that use for it never developed. Now caesium tubes are used in connection with talking moving pictures, but it is said that a simple and cheap device has been made to take their place for that service also. Perhaps some other use will soon be found for it.

Thallium compounds are poisonous and have recently been found to be extremely effective in poisoning gophers, which are a social menace on our West Coast as possible carriers of the fleas that transmit plague. It has recently gained a good deal of publicity through this use, for zealous nature-lovers have begun objecting to its use for this purpose. Though their objections do not seem to be well-founded, they have attracted much attention to this hitherto obscure mineral substance.

Finally there are a considerable number of what may be colloquially termed as "white hopes" in industry. Gallium is a grayish white metal that melts at summer temperatures, but only boils at about 3000°F. It would seem that there should be a use for it but none has been found, although it was discovered over fifty years ago. It was thought it could be used for high-temperature thermometers, but practical difficulties developed. Columbium (also known as niobium) has been known more than a century, but seems to have no use that tantalum will not better serve. Germanium is almost fifty years old, and it could be produced as a by-product of zinc refining if there were a known use for it. Scandium is even older, and indium has been known for sixty years. Various possibilities of using these metals have been suggested, but none of them have yet developed.

Hafnium, rhenium, and masurium, on the other hand, date only from the last decade and it is too early yet to know what use can be made of them.

CHAPTER IX

OUR MINERAL RESERVES

W<small>HEN</small> people talk, as they often do, of our mineral reserves they always have in mind the known but yet unexploited deposits of those minerals that we are now using so freely, discussed in preceding chapters. There is still another way of thinking of mineral reserves, and that is to consider the ones of which we have an abundant supply, but for which relatively little use has as yet been discovered.

Some years ago F. W. Clarke made an estimate of the average chemical composition of that part of the terrestrial globe which is conceivably within our reach. He included the crust of the earth to a depth of ten miles, the oceans, and the atmosphere. The latter, of course, did not contribute much to the total and although air is four-fifths nitrogen, that element only makes up two-ten-thousandths of the whole, falling into seventeenth place among the ninety elements that have been identified. There are only eight elements that rank above one-one-hundredth part of the whole mass estimated. The order in which they appear shows no correlation with their present social and economic importance. For example, we now require yearly more than twenty times as much carbon as we do iron, yet the quantity of iron in existence in the zone of Dr. Clarke's estimate is twenty-five times the amount of carbon.

It is not quantity alone that interests us, but rather availability for use. While the carbon is much less abundant, it is much more usable, for great quantities occur in the form of coal or petroleum, that are almost 100 per cent carbon. So long as carbon-rich minerals are freely available low-carbon mineral substances are of interest only to scientists; but they constitute a possible reserve. The same condition holds for iron; in this country a mineral that is less than one-half iron is not now a commercially practicable source of it, though in Europe material that is one-third iron is usable. The quantity of iron-bearing material as rich as that is relatively small, but it is enough for present demands, and as existing rich deposits now being exploited become exhausted the problem at first will be to decide between bringing distant supplies to existing facilities or moving the facilities to the supplies, rather than to find additional sources of iron.

What we shall in the future need to do about the minerals we use in large quantity is the problem of mineral supplies, as usually stated. The other aspect of the matter is perhaps no problem at all, since all we have to do with those minerals of which there is a large supply and but little present need is to let them alone. There they are, and there they will remain until we begin to call upon them. It is surprising, however, to learn how abundant some of them actually are. The most surprising is titanium, of which the quantity theoretically available is fifty per cent more than of carbon, our most useful mineral, and yet we only use about one-millionth part as much.

Titanium owes its relative abundance to its wide dissemination through the igneous rocks; it is relatively seldom that it is found in concentrated bodies. One form in which it occurs is over half titanium, but the commoner sources of it contain only one-eighth to one-quarter of the element. It is not so easy to obtain as some of the other minerals, therefore, but after all allowance has been made for that it must still be admitted that the principal reason why it remains in reserve is that it has as yet no outstanding uses. Its principal service is as a white paint pigment, but there are several white pigments that have long been in use, that serve man's needs satisfactorily, and compete with each other for the privilege of serving him most effectively. They might be compared with the various makes of automobiles, all of which give good service and each of which has some "talking point." Titanium pigment has its special advantages and its use has increased very rapidly of recent years but it is still small compared to the available supply of titanium.

Titanium alloys have found a limited application in steel manufacture and foundry practice, as it is helpful in making clean, sound metal, and serves as deoxidizer in brass and bronze foundries. Here also there are other means of accomplishing the same ends. Titanium was useful in arc-light carbons, but arc lighting is now almost obsolete except in "ultra-violet" lamps of which the electrodes contain 1.5 per cent titanium. It has various chemical uses, but none of them call for large amounts. Whether we shall ever find many and important uses for it no one can say; so far we have not, although almost a century and a half have passed since it was first recognized as an element.

Chlorine and bromine are lumped together by Clarke and immediately follow carbon, corresponding to about two-thirds its total quantity. The first is much the more abundant, as it is not only found in huge thick beds of salt, but is everywhere available in ocean water. Someone has estimated that if the oceans were evaporated they would yield 4,500,000 cubic miles of rock salt. In spite of that imposing figure most of our present supply of salt is derived from other sources because it happens to be commercially more practicable to produce pure salt from brines and salt beds than from sea water.

For many of the uses to which we put chlorine we require salt (sodium chloride), and the credit can not be claimed by either chlorine or sodium alone, since they must be combined to be useful. But in chemical manufacture we take salt apart so as to make other sodium and chlorine compounds. There are many of these, but it so happens that sodium and its compounds are more in demand than chlorine and its derivatives are. Almost everybody knows of the bleaching action of chlorine and its compounds, perhaps they do not realize that its biggest use for that purpose is in the production of pulp and paper. Another large use of chlorine is in the manufacture of artificial silk. Everybody who uses a swimming pool has smelled chlorine. The people who use carbon tetrachloride as a grease remover perhaps do not realize that its principal use in industry is as a solvent and as a fire-extinguisher rather than as a cleanser. Chlorine yields chlorides of many other things besides sodium, some of which have extremely important uses. Its uses are literally legion. Perhaps some people will think that I am wrong in suggesting that we have more of it than we are able yet to use, but nevertheless it is true.

There is no dispute, however, about its close associate, bromine. Both in salt deposits and in brines, bromine is associated with chlorine and as much of it as can be sold is produced as a by-product. In its properties it somewhat resembles chlorine; but there are relatively few human purposes for which it is sufficiently better to make much demand for it. Were it not for its usefulness in making "ethyl gas," in photography, and a small but important use in medicine, it would scarcely be used at all. Of course there is reason in arguing that the service it renders man through enabling him to do photographic work is so important that bromine is entitled to claim high rank among the useful elements. It gives his eyes mastery over time and space; nature enables him to see things that are before him at the time, he himself has found out how to see things that are far distant in space and time. He can even photograph things he cannot see. No one would deny that this is of transcendent importance, but it does not require much bromine to do it and the honor might with equal validity be claimed by silver. As a matter of fact there are numerous chemical salts that are affected by light and we could still make out after a fashion if we had neither silver nor bromine to do photography with. The point is that a very small fraction of the bromine available is sufficient to meet these needs. Five hundred to a thousand tons a year in the United States was enough to supply all needs until 1928, when it began to be used to make the ethylene dibromide required in making "ethyl gasoline." In 1930 some 4000 tons were sold, which indicates the quantitative importance of the latter use. This 400 per cent increase in two years is an excellent instance of how the discovery of a new use increases mineral consumption. Of course bromine's important use as a sedative in medicine amounts to very little from the quantitative standpoint, as a dose is so small.

The third member of the same family, iodine, is even less in demand, except for its various uses in medicine and in the iodide method for quantitative analysis in chemistry, it serves no purpose that requires more than very small amounts. It could be recovered as a by-product in the production of Chile saltpeter in much larger amounts than can now be sold. The nitrate producers have done much intelligent and well-directed work to increase the demand for iodine, but even if the annual consumption is thus doubled it will still not be very large. Almost the whole of the thousand tons or so produced yearly in the world comes from Chile, and it is worth about $9000 per ton. Most people know how important small quantities of it are in food and that a lack of it produces goitre in men, but it is not generally known that some animals often suffer from iodine deficiency.

Works on the chemistry of agriculture usually say something like this: "Of all the minerals necessary for plant growth the compounds containing phosphorus are most liable to be deficient." To a careless reader this may seem to mean that phosphorus is scarce in nature, but as a matter of fact it is more than twice as abundant as sulphur. What the agriculturist is trying to say is that it is not easily available to plants, the reason being that it does not occur in a form in which they can use it. The minerals in which it occurs are quite insoluble. Animals eat the plants and use their phosphorus content to build bone. In doing so, they not only keep it indefinitely but also turn it back into insoluble calcium phosphate. If bones are ground fine and the meal applied near the roots of the plants they can, with some difficulty, again utilize it. The chemist is more helpful, he treats the insoluble natural phosphate with acid and converts it into a soluble "super-phosphate." When it was found that calcium phosphate occurs in huge deposits in many parts of the world the problem resolved itself into the economic one as to whether the farmer, by using phosphate fertilizer, could grow enough larger crops to repay him for his outlay on it. Much of the cost to the farmer is the freight involved in bringing the phosphate from where it is found to where he wants to use it. If it is put into a concentrated form it has to be diluted again before using, because of the danger of killing the plants by supplying them with too concentrated salts. Thus there are many interesting technical problems involved, but they are aside from the basic fact that there is plenty of phosphorus in the world, even for fertilizer purposes, which is its principal use. Were it not that animals put it into a form not easily available to plants the quantities they need would simply circulate, being put into use by the growing plants, and released again by their decay.

The already known reserves of phosphate minerals of usable quality are very large, something like eleven billion tons of material that is over 58 per cent tri-calcium phosphate. Our own state of Idaho alone is estimated to contain some five billion tons. Thus there is not only plenty of phosphorus in the world, but great deposits of usable quality. More than nine-tenths of our present production of phosphate mineral is for fertilizer purposes. The other uses that absorb the remainder are multitudinous. Phosphorus sesqui-sulphide in making matches, orthophosphoric acid in phosphate soft drinks (and for many other purposes), monocalcium phosphate in baking powder and self-rising flour, and trisodic phosphate in cleaning preparations are the uses that touch most on the daily life of all of us. Phosphorus is added to iron and steel sometimes to make the metal very fluid in casting. It appears in rat poison, tracer bullets, incendiary shells and fire-works. We have indeed many and diverse uses for it, but none of them, except fertilizers, calls for large amounts. Even for fertilizer purposes it is estimated that more than enough to supply our needs for the next 2000 years is already known, while more may be discovered.

Manganese comes next after phosphorus in the list of minerals according to their relative abundance, being a little less than twice as abundant as sulphur. Here again our problem is not to find minerals that contain it, but those high enough in their content to be commercially usable; ore that contains less than 45 per cent cannot ordinarily be sold. Since the principal use of manganese is in connection with steel it is an odd fact that Nature has laid down its best manganese deposits in countries that either produce but little steel, or none at all. It is also an odd fact that the most of it used

in steel making does not go into the steel.   The
operation may be likened to washing the hands,
for which soap is used but no soap remains on the
hands after the operation is finished.   Possibly
some way of accomplishing the desired result without using manganese may be discovered, but at
present this is its principal use.   Steel containing
12 to 14 per cent manganese is so remarkably hard
and tough that it has many important uses.   City
dwellers have seen it in the shining light-colored
X-shaped pieces of rail where street car tracks
intersect each other.   The frogs where railway
tracks intersect are made of it, and it has many
other uses where resistance to abrasion and shock
are important enough to justify a somewhat
increased cost.   The black material inside the
cells of a dry battery, familiar to small boys who
have broken them to see what they are like inside,
is manganese dioxide of such high quality that
only the purest natural material or a chemically
purified one will serve this purpose.   Boiling lin-
seed oil with the same material yields the "dryer"
that is added to paint to cause it to dry more
quickly than it otherwise would.

The color of an amethyst is due to the presence
of manganese in what would otherwise be white
quartz.   Manganese is used to impart a somewhat
similar color to china and glassware and is also

used, strangely enough, to make glass white. The materials from which glass is made commonly contain enough iron to give the glass a yellowish tint but a slight addition of manganese changes the iron into a colorless compound. It has many important uses in the chemical laboratory but all together our uses for manganese call for an annual output of material containing about 2,000,000 tons of the metal, and 90 per cent of that is required for its uses in the steel industry. In short, it is twice as abundant as sulphur and we use less than half as much, most of it for a single purpose.

Calcium, magnesium, sodium, and potassium exist in the earth's crust in about the same relative proportions. Clarke rated them respectively as Ca, 3.51 per cent; Mg, 2.50 per cent; Na, 2.28 per cent; and K, 2.23 per cent of the material taken into account in his calculation. But we do not use them in anything like the same proportions. In the United States we use about 35,000,000 tons of calcium annually, mostly in the form of limestone, but only about 80,000 tons of magnesium. Of sodium we use about 3,500,000 tons, mostly in the form of salt, while of potassium we use only about 300,000 tons, mostly as fertilizer. The basic reason is that the chemical properties of magnesium so resemble those of calcium, and the properties of potassium are enough like those of sodium so that the one most easily available is the one most used.   That is not an accurate statement; no generalization ever is.   One of the principal uses of calcium is in the form of limestone as flux in iron blast furnaces.   Magnesium would not serve that purpose.   Another big use is as stone in building construction.   The natural stones containing magnesium would not serve that purpose as well, either.   Potassium, on the other hand, is so much harder to obtain in usable form, and is therefore so much more expensive, that it is only used where its effects are so different from those of sodium that the more expensive material is required.

Magnesium has indeed no very large use except as a refractory in furnace construction, as has been described on page 90.   But even important recent developments in the technique of magnesite brick-making are not likely to push our annual consumption of it up to where it even approximates some of the apparently minor uses of limestone, such as in the soda process of paper-making.

In fairness to magnesium it should be added that we use from 300,000 to 500,000 tons yearly of what is reported as "refractory lime," made from the natural material dolomite, in which magnesium and calcium occur in about equal proportion. Dolomite is also used in other ways, altogether amounting to about 1,500,000 tons yearly. The principle remains true, however, that there is no large use for magnesium compounds except as a refractory substance, and much of that as a calcium-magnesium mixture. It has scores of other uses, one of the most interesting being as a constituent of alloys that need to be lighter than aluminum. As a metal, its principal use once was in taking flash-light pictures, but it is being displaced for that purpose by the new flash-lamp in which aluminum foil is used and its main use now is in aircraft manufacture. An important use of calcined magnesite is in making the insulating coverings that are put on steam pipes, that are a familiar sight in every basement, but which are most extensively used in industrial plants. For this purpose it is mixed with asbestos fiber. The ability to transmit steam without its losing its heat content has made central heating and steam supply plants practicable. In large cities this is already an organized business and it is quite probable that it may be greatly extended. Some of the carbon dioxide used in making soda water is produced from magnesite rather than limestone, because it yields a marketable by-product. But after all these things, and many others that might be added, have been said, it still remains true that our reserve of magnesium is as big as that of calcium, but we are drawing on it much less heavily.

A curious situation exists as regards potassium. It occurs in the igneous rocks with sodium, but when these rocks disintegrate the sodium tends to go into solution and eventually finds its way into the sea. By the evaporation of ancient seas immense deposits of salt have been formed all over the world, so it is nowhere hard to obtain. The potassium in the original rocks, on the other hand, mostly goes into those rather indefinite minerals that are loosely classed under the general name of clay, which not only form clay deposits, but yield the rocks known as shales, which in turn by metamorphic processes give rise to the more familiar slates. Clay also furnishes the binding material in various sedimentary rocks, such as the argillaceous sandstones. These mineral substances are so abundant that they represent a vast potential reserve of potassium. Unfortunately the proportion of it present in them is so small that there is no practicable way of recovering it from them, though much study has been devoted to that problem. Our only commercially practicable sources of potassium are the beds of potash salts that are found very sparingly around the world, as compared to salt. When sea water evaporates the salt first crystallizes out, and later the potash compounds follow them. The best known deposits of these salts are near Stassfurt, in northern Germany, and so much has been written about them that they hardly need description. For a long time it was supposed that this was the only deposit of the kind in the world, but protracted search not only revealed workable deposits in Alsace, but also deposits in a number of other countries, notably Spain, Poland, and Russia, that are at least of some value. Much effort was devoted to the search for domestic sources of potash in this country. Finally it was commercially produced from Searles lake, in California. A petroleum company, recently in sinking a well accidentally discovered an important deposit of potash in New Mexico. The deposit there is about twice as rich in potash as the German deposits and by 1933 will possibly make us independent of foreign sources of supply.

Potassium has three kinds of uses. The most important is as fertilizer. Plants can get all the sodium they want from the soil, but they cannot do as well with potassium, because the minerals in which it occurs are too insoluble. So the farmer feeds them with soluble potash salts, which he has to buy usually, since although they occur in manure and wood ashes the supply of those two things is not enough for the agriculturist's needs. Another use for potassium is in places where sodium would otherwise do as well, except that it has a greater tendency to absorb moisture from the air. For that reason we have to use potassium nitrate in making gunpowder, for example. The third use of potassium is for chemical purposes where it is the only thing that will do, such as the "cream of tartar" sometimes used in baking powder, and the various potassium compounds used in chemistry. Ninety per cent of the potassium we require we use as fertilizer, and much of the rest of it goes into explosive manufacture and the making of potassium chlorate. It was lucky that we did not have any big need for it, for until recently it has been difficult to obtain, at a reasonable cost, as much as we needed. Now we seem to have a pretty good control of our supply and can begin to use it more freely. Maybe some day we will be able to unlock the stores of it that are now unavailable to us.

This by no means exhausts the list of mineral substances of which the apparent supply is large in proportion to the uses for which we now require them. But enough has been said to indicate there are many of them. To attempt to forecast what uses may be found for them would be as difficult a task as that imposed on his father by the small boy, who listened with wonder to his senior's account of the many things we now use that were not available when his parent was a boy, and then, with shrewd foresight, asked his father to tell him what we are not now using but would be employing when the boy was a man.

One thing that may be said, however, is to bring up the question of substitutes. In an earlier chapter it was pointed out that many mineral substances can be used in constructing the roofs of buildings. It is seldom that we have so great a diversity of alternative materials available. In some cases there is a great difference between the thing used and the next best thing. But one can never forsee when a new bit of knowledge or of technique will make something else equally available. A good example of this is the way chromium plating has recently come to compete with nickel plating. Fifty years ago no one could have imagined the concrete roads of today. There is therefore not only plenty of opportunity for research and development, but an abundant store of mineral raw materials for which new or increased uses may be found.

CHAPTER X

MINERALS AND CIVILIZATION

Since long experience indicates that some of the audience, at the conclusion of any lecture, go away believing that the lecturer's views are the direct opposite of those that he has actually expressed, it seems reasonable to suppose that some readers will lay down this little volume believing that my endeavor has been to prove that minerals are an index of civilization; the more civilized a people are the more minerals do they use. At the risk of seeming to elaborate the obvious, let me reiterate that that has not been my purpose. The civilization of the 20th Century may fairly be characterized as a mineral civilization, it might also be described as a reading civilization or flying civilization. In each case the adjective would be justified because recent times are in marked contrast to preceding ages in that respect.

In these pages the aim has been to point out that minerals are, in our modern civilization, not only used in relatively larger amounts but in a greatly diversified number of ways and to serve many new purposes. They have improved our human life in a variety of ways, the most striking being the enormous multiplication of man's natural capacities. His voice, originally capable of being heard a mile or so, can now be heard around the world, not only while he is yet speaking but long afterward as well. Once he could see only a few miles, now not only are sights and scenes visible at distant places, and action visible long after it has ceased, but things which men had never seen have been revealed to them. Curiously enough, smell, taste, and feeling have not had their effectiveness multiplied as have the other two senses; at least not in the same way. The argument might perhaps be made that modern transportation, storage, and preservation facilities have made it possible for man to smell, taste and feel things formerly entirely beyond his reach.

The effect of minerals on man's abilities has been even more striking than its intensification of his senses. His ability to transport himself and his goods from place to place has been greatly improved. The speed of travel has been multiplied by ten in the past century, whereas in all preceding time it had scarcely more than doubled. The personal effort required in travel has been greatly reduced, and also its discomfort. Messages can be sent at a greatly increased velocity, at a small fraction of the former cost, and with less possibility of error in transmission. It would take too much space to develop that theme fully, and we will concentrate upon the most important consideration, the way minerals have increased man's capacity to do the work necessary for the satisfaction of his needs and the accomplishment of his purposes.

In the earliest times if a man wanted anything done he had to do it himself. Later he subjugated other men and made them work for him as slaves, he also tamed animals and forced them to work for him. There was but little economic advantage, except to the individual thus benefitted, in so doing. A group of a million human beings can do only a limited amount of work and it is only by unequal division of the total product of that work that one man is able to have more than he could get for himself. There was some economy in the organization of effort, for one slave operating a punkah could cool a dozen people with less effort than they together would expend in fanning themselves, but this advantage springs mainly from the mechanical contrivance and only secondarily from a concentration of effort that is equally productive of advantage in a free society. Slavery did not benefit the group as a whole except through transferring the planning of work to the better minds, and there is more than a little doubt whether the masters had better minds than many of the slaves. There was also relatively little economic advantage in the domestication of work animals. Chiefly it lay in the fact that the animals subsisted on food that men could not utilize, instead of making a demand on the common food supply, as the slaves did. Anyone who has lived on a farm knows that there is much work involved in taking care of and feeding animals, and can well believe the estimate that 26,000,000 acres of land in the United States, formerly devoted to growing food for animals, has recently been made available for growing food for men by the modern transition from work animals to mechanical power farming.

The development of the steam engine was basically a new way for using coal, of which the uses up to that time had been rather limited. Now it is our principal source of power supply. Over 90 per cent of the work done in the United States today is done by mechanical means; a little less than two-thirds of it by coal, and about one-third of it by petroleum and gas, those round figures leaving space for the approximately 5 per cent that is done by water power. Instead of depending on animal sources of power, utilizing the energy in plants, which had received it from the

sun's radiation, men learned to utilize the preserved energy of the sun in concentrated form.

This new way of doing work had three important
phases. It enabled work to be done that could
not be done before. Three or four men, at the
most, can strike a blow simultaneously on one
spot, but a machine can easily strike with the force
of ten thousand men. Three hundred thousand
men could exert the pull of a modern big locomo-
tive, but could not simultaneously travel at the
rate of forty miles an hour. It thus made possible
the seemingly impossible. It also transformed
men's status. Now, on the average, they are
directors of work rather than workers, in the
sense in which a ditch-digger or a hod-carrier is a
worker. It would be more accurate to say they
have been promoted to more important work,
since the planning and direction of work is more
important and socially valuable than its performance, as we shall see in a moment.

Finally, it greatly increased the output of work
of a given group of people. By making certain
justifiable assumptions it can be computed that
the work done in the United States in 1930 was
equivalent to that which could be done by forty
times as many people as live here. Consequently
the people of the United States can have a higher

standard of living than those of any other country.
It is not surprising to find that estimates of the
per capita wealth of the countries of the world
show a ratio that corresponds to the per capita
work done in those countries.

Recent events have shown that those who
thought the sweeping changes thus brought about
in men's way of living would be easy to manage
and control were greatly mistaken. With a capacity to produce far more than all of us together
want, and without a desire, except on the part of
the relatively few criminals, to deprive others of
their due share, we find ourselves in a position
where many people are without the means of sub-
sistence. The mass effect is almost terrifying.
When everybody walked if some had to stop the
others kept on, but when a train stops every passenger is stopped. Similarly, in modern industry,
great numbers of people are simultaneously thrown
out of work. In an agricultural civilization nobody made a very good living, but they could
always make some kind of living. In an industrial
civilization, where people work to produce what
they cannot personally use, if they cannot market
their product they are without means to make any
living. We seem in much the same situation as a
little boy who, thinking he has mastered the art of
riding a bicycle, shortly thereafter finds himself in
the ditch.

So much has recently been written and spoken about this, which is for many individuals not simply a problem but a personal tragedy, that nothing more will be said about it here than to point out that one factor in it seems to be a persistence of the slave psychology. This exhibits itself in two ways. Some Eighteenth century and early Nineteenth century thinkers on social problems fell into the error of supposing that the whole value of a product resided in the human labor expended on its production. The logical deduction from this erroneous premise was that the workers should get as their wage the full, or nearly full value of the product. These thinkers completely failed to make the cognate deduction that when a machine makes a product without the aid of human labor the machine should get the full value of the product. Actually, of course, the owner of the machine does not get the full value of the product, but has to pay for its operation and repair, and to replace it when it is worn out. It is possible to conceive of an enterprise in which all the work is done by machines without any human help, and yet after all the expenses of operation are met there is nothing left over from the sale value of the product for the owner of the machines and accessory equipment. Mechanical engineers can understand this very easily, because they are well aware that it is often cheaper to generate power in a steam plant from purchased coal than it is in a water-power plant, where there is no expense for fuel, simply because the construction and equipment cost of a water-power plant is so much higher than that of a steam plant. The general public finds it very difficult to understand, however, and thinks that water-power sites are tremendously valuable assets that should be carefully treasured.

Another error of many economic thinkers is in ignoring the social value of planning and control. Only in the case of invention is it clearly recognized. A man who has discovered a way in which to do something with half the expenditure of human effort usually required would be within his rights if he concealed his discovery from everyone else. If he tells them he is making them a present of something valuable to them. Obviously he cannot demand the full value as the price of telling them, since they might subsequently have found it out themselves. The patent system is a reasonable human approximation in securing for an inventor some part of the social value of his work, while permitting society to reap the main benefit from it.

So little is the social value of planning in the ordinary conduct of work recognized that someone recently asked me whether an engineer should be considered a productive worker in modern industry. It seems absurd that such a question could be asked. If a piece of work could ordinarily be done by 1000 men in 1000 days, or a million man-days, and an engineer plans it so it can be done in 750,000 man-days, he is obviously the most productive worker of all, for he has done a quarter of the total work. The elimination of useless work is the engineer's greatest contribution to social welfare, but its importance tends to be overlooked because the work that would have had to be done, but was not, is never visible and is not easily visualized.

In the same way the importance of management in modern industry is easily overlooked. Effective planning and management sometimes reaps huge profits, though employing only a small capital. Certainly these profits do not belong to the workers in the enterprise, for they would have worked in the same way for an unprofitable as for a profitable enterprise. The basic error of socialistic thinking is in failing to see that there was a risk of failure in the enterprise which the planner and manager was willing to take because there was also hope of gain. Without the hope of gain he would not have incurred the risk. Socialist Russia has already found that its greatest difficulty is in finding men willing to accept responsibility for plans that may fail.

Estimation of the value of work that involves only mental energy is exceedingly difficult. Anyone can see that a worker who produces ten articles in a day is better than one who produces only five, but few people can evaluate the man who sits all day with his heels on his desk, thinking. He may be the most valuable man in the enterprise and he may be an absolute idler. If he sits there a long time without visible result the latter presumption becomes strong, yet it might be profitable to tolerate him for years if he eventually produces something to justify it.

The rôle of minerals in this social process is a dual one; they offer possibilities for creative work and provide the means of realizing them. They are like the strings of a violin that both enable a composer to create a new work, and permit an orchestra to render it for the benefit of an audience. Like the strings, they are passive instruments and have no responsibility for the use that is made of them. This seems so obvious as not to need mention, and yet much current discussion of the radio seems to assume that the instruments and technique are somehow to blame for the programs that are sent over the air. The critics are as mentally confused as the King who used to kill the messengers who brought him bad news.

This brings us to the final question and answer. Is man any better off because he has learned to utilize minerals so as to multiply his capacities. The question cannot be answered unless some clear definition of what is meant by "better off" is provided. Is a man better off because the probability that he will die early of disease has been greatly lessened and the possibility that he will die of some diseases almost eliminated? Is a man better off because he can be protected from the cold of winter and the heat of summer? Is a man better off because he is no longer almost wholly dependent on the light of the sun? Is a man better off because he can talk to his wife or child, a thousand miles away? Most such questions need only to be clearly phrased to answer themselves, and the final residue is a query as to whether people are any happier because of the developments that we have been discussing.

I have often wondered why no one seems ever to have replied to the old question as to how many angels can stand on the point of a needle, with the self-evident fact that no one has ever seen even one angel standing on the point of a needle. Happiness does not reside in the things we have been discussing. They may operate to produce happiness and unhappiness. The friends of a patient are happy if a doctor, brought by an airplane, arrives in time to save his life. The family of an air mail pilot are desolate if he crashes on some stormy trip. The owner of an automobile rejoices in its comfortable speed but is disconsolate if he accidentally injures a child with it. There is nothing new in that, however; long before the era of machinery an emperor was as heartbroken over the death of his son as a slave was at the death of his child. Happiness and the things we have been discussing are simply incommensurate quantities.

Thus at the end we go back to our beginning. The century just passed has been marked by a notable increase in the ways men use minerals to accomplish their purposes, and an even more notable increase in the quantities and kinds of minerals thus used. This progress has given rise to many new problems. One of these is whether the supply of minerals easily available for use will be adequate to meet the demands upon them. Just now this is obscured by a present capacity to produce them, (and almost everything else), in larger quantities than we currently need, which has created a major social crisis. Underneath them both, and eventually demanding solution, are the problems arising out of the extremely irregular distribution of minerals on the earth's surface, so that no close correlation exists between the needs of national groups and their means of supply. Even a brief discussion of those problems

would require another book as large as this.   For-
tunately for the United States, we are the best
situated of any nation in that regard and can well
afford to take the lead in seeking a sound solution
of these problems without fearing suspicion of
seeking only our national advantage.

OTHER TITLES IN A CENTURY OF PROGRESS SERIES

THE STORY OF A BILLION YEARS   (*Geology*)
  WILLIAM O. HOTCHKISS, President Michigan College of Mining
    and Technology, Houghton
CHEMISTRY TRIUMPHANT   (*Industrial Chemistry*)
  WILLIAM J. HALE, Dow Chemical Company, Midland, Michigan
THE QUEEN OF THE SCIENCES   (*Mathematics*)
  E. T. BELL, Department of Mathematics, California Institute
    of Technology, Pasadena
FRONTIERS OF MEDICINE   (*Medicine*)
  MORRIS FISHBEIN, Editor of Journal of American Medical
    Association
ALL ABOUT OIL   (*Petroleum*)
  GUSTAV EGLOFF, Universal Oil Products Company, Chicago, Ill.
ADJUSTMENT AND MASTERY   (*Psychology*)
  ROBERT S. WOODWORTH, Department of Psychology, Columbia
    University, New York City
THE TREATMENT OF STEEL AND PEOPLE   (*Steel Treating*)
  G. M. EATON, Director of Research, Spang, Chalfant & Com-
    pany, Inc., Ambridge, Pennsylvania

LIST PRICE $1.00 PER VOLUME

Sans Tache

Sans Tache

IN THE "elder days of art" each artist or craftsman enjoyed the privilege of independent creation. He carried through a process of manufacture from beginning to end. The scribe of the days before the printing press was such a craftsman. So was the printer in the days before the machine process. He stood or fell, as a craftsman, by the merit or demerit of his finished product.

Modern machine production has added much to the worker's productivity and to his material welfare; but it has deprived him of the old creative distinctiveness. His work is merged in the work of the team, and lost sight of as something representing him and his personality.

Many hands and minds contribute to the manufacture of a book, in this day of specialization. There are seven distinct major processes in the making of a book: The type must first be set; by the monotype method, there are two processes, the "keyboarding" of the MS and the casting of the type from the perforated paper rolls thus produced. Formulas and other intricate work must be hand-set; then the whole brought together ("composed") in its true order, made into pages and forms. The results must be checked by proof reading at each stage. Then comes the "make-ready" and press-run and finally the binding into volumes.

All of these processes, except that of binding into cloth or leather covers, are carried on under our roof.

The motto of the Waverly Press is *Sans Tache*. Our ideal is to manufacture books *"without blemish"*—worthy books, worthily printed, with worthy typography—books to which we shall be proud to attach our imprint, made by craftsmen who are willing to accept open responsibility for their work, and who are entitled to credit for creditable performance.

The printing craftsman of today is quite as much a craftsman as his predecessor. There is quite as much discrimination between poor work and good. We are of the opinion that the individuality of the worker should not be wholly lost. The members of our staff who have contributed their skill of hand and brain to this volume are:

Keyboard: Viola Schneider.

Casters: Ernest Wann, Charles Aher, Kenneth Brown, Henry Lee, Mahlon Robinson, Charles Fick, George Bullinger, Martin Griffen, Norwood Eaton, George Smith.

Composing Room: Arthur Baker, Charles Bittman, John Crabill, Robert Lambert, Emerson Madairy, William Sanders, Vernon Thomas, Anthony Wagner, Edward Rice, Richard King, Henry Shea, George Moss, Theodore Nilson.

Proof Room: Alice Reuter, Mary Reed, Ruth Jones, Audrey Knight, Angeline Johnson, Shirley Seidel, Dorothy Fick, Betty Williams, Alice Grabau, Catherine Dudley, Virginia Williams, Evelyn Rogers, Louisa Westcott, Roland Orth.

Press Room: Hugh Gardner, Henry Augsburg, Henry Hager, Emil Beres.

Cutter: William Armiger.

Folders: Laurence Krug, Clifton Hedley.

A CENTURY OF PROGRESS
SERIES

●

A series of volumes by well-known
scholars presenting the essential
features of those fundamental sciences which are the foundation
stones of modern industry

●